Hands-on Culture of WEST AFRICA

Kate O' Halloran
illustrations by Lloyd Birmingham

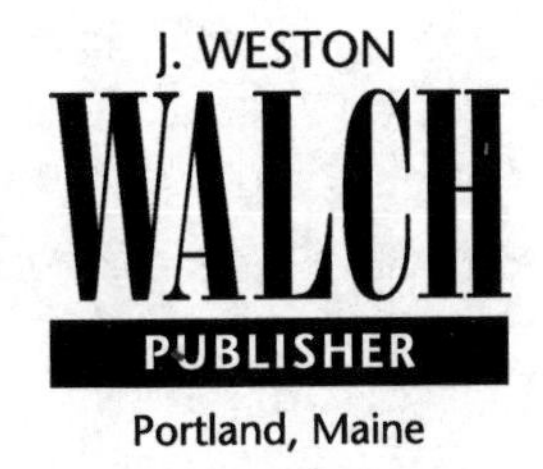

Portland, Maine

Dedication

For Aoife, who is Abayomi.

User's Guide
to
Walch Reproducible Books

As part of our general effort to provide educational materials which are as practical and economical as possible, we have designated this publication a "reproducible book." The designation means that purchase of the book includes purchase of the right to limited reproduction of all pages on which this symbol appears:

Here is the basic Walch policy: We grant to individual purchasers of this book the right to make sufficient copies of reproducible pages for use by all students of a single teacher. This permission is limited to a single teacher, and does not apply to entire schools or school systems, so institutions purchasing the book should pass the permission on to a single teacher. Copying of the book or its parts for resale is prohibited.

Any questions regarding this policy or requests to purchase further reproduction rights should be addressed to:

Permissions Editor
J. Weston Walch, Publisher
321 Valley Street • P. O. Box 658
Portland, Maine 04104-0658

1 2 3 4 5 6 7 8 9 10

ISBN 0-8251-3087-5

Printed in the United States of America

CONTENTS

How to Use This Book

This book, like the others in the Hands-On Culture series by J.Weston Walch, Publisher, has been designed to help middle school teachers integrate the study of a culture into the curriculum. Textbooks can teach students about the history and geography of an area, but to gain any real understanding, students must also be exposed to the art and traditions of a culture.

Hands-on Culture of West Africa provides 18 ready-to-use activities to help you do just that. Through the projects in this book, students will be exposed to some common phrases in Wolof, to the writing and counting systems used in West Africa, to West African cuisine, and to the art and literature of West Africa.

Throughout this book the focus is on traditional culture. That is because so much of West Africa's culture, even today, is based on tradition. Learning about the aspects of West African culture examined here will help students understand the culture as a whole. Sources like the Internet also provide excellent routes for students to learn about West Africa today.

Of course, many important elements of traditional West African culture are not included in this book. The mask-making and dancing traditions of West Africa, some fabric arts like *adire eleko,* and many other aspects of culture would make excellent research projects as part of a unit on the culture of West Africa to extend the projects presented here.

Most of the projects in this book work well either as individual projects or as group activities. When a project requires the setting up of a work station, as in the adinkra cloth and cooking projects, you may find it best to divide the class into groups and set up several work areas. You may also find a group approach helpful for some of the other projects. As students deal with such unfamiliar material as the Yoruba counting system, they may find it less intimidating to work together to find solutions.

By their nature, all these projects are interdisciplinary. All are appropriate for a social studies class. Most are appropriate for an art class. Some activities are also appropriate for other subject areas; the correlation chart on page *vii* presents these links. Some activities could be done in several different classes. The Okumpa play activity on page 54 and the adinkra cloth activity on page 39 are example of this type of activity. For the Okumpa play, the background could be given in a social studies class, satire and caricature could be explained and the play could be written in English class, the masks could be made in art class, and the songs could be written and rehearsed in music class. For the adinkra cloth activity, the background could be given in social studies, the discussion of symmetry could be given in math class, and the stamps could be made in art class.

If you are teaching about West Africa as part of an interdisciplinary team, each teacher can teach the activities appropriate to his or her domain. All the projects have been structured so that the teacher presenting the activity does not need to know either the historical context for an activity or the procedure for doing the project. Full background details are provided where needed. You can share some or all of this information with students if you wish, but it is not necessary for student completion of the project. The step-by-step student instructions for the activities should need no further explanation. All activities have been tested with middle and high school students.

To motivate students, and continue the theme of West African culture, you may wish to tell them that gift giving is an important feature of the culture. It is considered a sign of prestige to give gifts, and gift giving establishes a relationship between people. You might incorporate this custom into your classroom with small gifts or candy for the first group to finish the Nigerian names project correctly, or for the group with the most interesting version of the West African proverbs.

To help demonstrate the process, you may find it helpful to keep one or two examples of student work for each activity. The next time you present the activity, show the student work as models. When dealing with unfamiliar material, it can help students to have a general idea of what is expected of them.

Finally, check out the resources in your community. Many communities have members who have come from West Africa and are happy to share their knowledge with students. West African exchange students, who can often demonstrate various arts and who can at least talk briefly about West Africa and expose students to some of the languages of West Africa, are another resource.

I hope that you—and your students—enjoy this book, and that it helps deepen your students' understanding and appreciation of West Africa.

Subject Area Correlation

	Music	Math	Science	Language Arts	Art	Social Studies
Money in West Africa: Cedi, Dalasi, Naira		x			x	x
West African Folktales				x		x
Music of West Africa	x					x
Benin: Appliqué Art of Dahomey				x	x	x
Burkina Faso: Building a House		x	x		x	x
Côte d'Ivoire: Baule Gold Plating					x	x
Ghana: Kente Cloth			x		x	x
Ghana: Akan Coffins					x	x
Ghana: Adinkra Cloth			x		x	x
Ghana and Côte d'Ivoire: Akan Gold Weights					x	x
Mali: Griots and the Story of Sundiata				x		x
Nigeria: Proverbs				x		x
Nigeria: What's in a Name?				x		x
Nigeria: Humor and Politics	x			x	x	x
Nigeria: Yoruba Numbers				x		x
Senegal: A Conversation in Wolof						x
Sierra Leone: The Game of Haba Gaba		x				x
Jollof Rice and Fufu: Cooking of West Africa						x

Money in West Africa: Cedi, Dalasi, Naira

OBJECTIVES

Social Studies

- Students will become familiar with some of the exports of the nations of West Africa.
- Students will understand the connection between available resources and the economy.
- Students will differentiate among various forms of exchange and money.

Math

- Students will practice converting from one currency to another.

Art

- Students will design and create currency.

MATERIALS

Money in West Africa handout
paper
pencils
colored pencils, markers, paints
scissors

BACKGROUND

One interesting twist sometimes arises in this simulation. Two countries both export the same item, but each assigns a different value to the item. Students may find this confusing and think that the same item should always have the same absolute value. Encourage them to realize that the same item can have a different value to different people, depending on its availability.

Students should also be encouraged to look closely at the lists of items exported. Some countries have only a few exports. Some have far more. Can students make any guesses about the economy of these countries, based on the amount of things they export? What about the types of things exported? Encourage students to speculate on the different economic strengths of a country like Liberia, which exports iron, rubber, diamonds, and gold, and one like Mali, which exports cotton, livestock, and peanuts.

Procedure

1. Distribute the handout and discuss it with students.
2. Model each stage of the activity. You can use either one of the currencies on the handout or the fictional currency given in the student procedure—the minim, with an exchange rate of 10 to the dollar, and exports of diamonds, gold, and peanuts.
3. Divide the class into groups. You may assign a country to each group, or you may wish to allow students to choose their own countries. If you feel that this activity may be too challenging for your students, assign all groups countries that use the franc CFA as a currency. They can still experiment with imports and exports and an unfamiliar currency without having to convert from one currency to another via a dollar exchange rate. In other classes, you may want to limit the number of groups using countries with the franc CFA as currency, so that the activity remains challenging.
4. Students should proceed as directed on the handout.

Variation

If time permits, have each group trade with a total of three other groups, then see how the goods they hold have changed. Do they still have any of their original goods? Did they receive any of their original goods back in a later trade? What is the monetary value of the goods they now hold based on the currencies of origin?

Extension

These figures are based on the official rate of exchange as of August 1996. Since exchange rates change daily, these rates may be very different today. Have students research the current rates of exchange between these currencies and the dollar to see how much—or whether—they have changed.

Assessment

Did students create currency and export cards, and successfully carry out at least two transactions using a West African currency?

Bonus Question

These countries were once under French rule.

Name ______________________________ Date ______________

Money in West Africa: Cedi, Dalasi, Naira

Africa is a continent, not a country. It is made up of many different peoples, each with their own history, culture, and language. Before Europeans came to Africa, most of these different groups ruled themselves. They only connected with other groups for trade or for war. Great empires rose and conquered other peoples. Then they were conquered in their turn, and the empires faded away.

When people in Europe became aware of Africa, they saw it as a great resource. They took gold and diamonds from its soil and trees from its forests. They took people from Africa—men, women, and children—to work on plantations in America. And to keep control of Africa, they divided it up among themselves. The French took control of some parts. The English and the Germans and the Portuguese took others. They divided the continent into different countries and agreed among themselves on borders. The borders generally didn't have anything to do with the people who lived in an area. Often, the new borders cut right through cultural groups, leaving some members of a group living in one country, others in another.

Today, Africa is once again ruled by Africans. But it is still divided into countries and the borders still cut across ethnic groups. This sometimes causes unrest within a country. But the different peoples of Africa are trying to find positive solutions.

Like other countries around the world, the countries of West Africa produce more than they need of some things. When they have a surplus, they can sell it to other countries as exports. The money they receive for these exports can be used to buy things they need from other countries. These purchases are called imports.

But most countries use different money systems. They have to work out how much one country's money, or currency, is worth in the other country's money before they can make a deal.

The table on the next page lists 14 of the countries of West Africa. It shows each country's main exports. It also names the unit of money each country uses and the dollar exchange rate for that money. The dollar exchange rate is the amount of money you would have to give to equal a dollar. If the dollar exchange rate were seven, that would mean you would have to pay seven units of that money to get a dollar. It also means that one dollar would buy seven units in that currency.

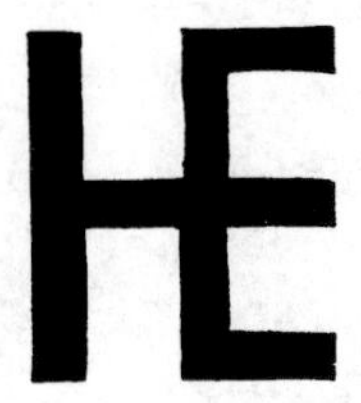

(continued)

Name ______________________ Date ______________

Money in West Africa: Cedi, Dalasi, Naira *(continued)*

Country	Currency	Exchange rate/$	Main exports
Benin	franc CFA	489.22	petroleum, cotton, cocoa, sugar, palm oil, peanuts, cement
Burkina Faso	franc CFA	489.22	cotton, karite nuts, livestock, gold, cotton
Côte d'Ivoire	franc CFA	489.22	cocoa, coffee, petroleum products, timber, fruit
Gambia	dalasi	9.825	peanuts, peanut products, fish, fish products, hides, palm oil
Ghana	cedi	1680	cocoa, gold, timber, bauxite, manganese, diamonds
Guinea	Guinea franc	997	bauxite, alumina, fruit, diamonds, coffee, hides
Guinea-Bissau	peso	18036	fish, peanuts, coconuts
Liberia	Liberian dollar	1	iron ore, rubber, timber, coffee, cocoa, palm oil, diamonds, gold
Mali	franc CFA	489.22	cotton, livestock, peanuts
Niger	franc CFA	489.22	uranium, livestock, vegetables
Nigeria	naira	22	petroleum, cocoa, palm oil, rubber, cotton, tin
Senegal	franc CFA	489.22	fish products, peanuts, phosphates, chemicals
Sierra Leone	leone	870	titanium ore, diamonds, bauxite, cocoa, ginger
Togo	franc CFA	489.22	phosphates, cotton, cocoa, coffee

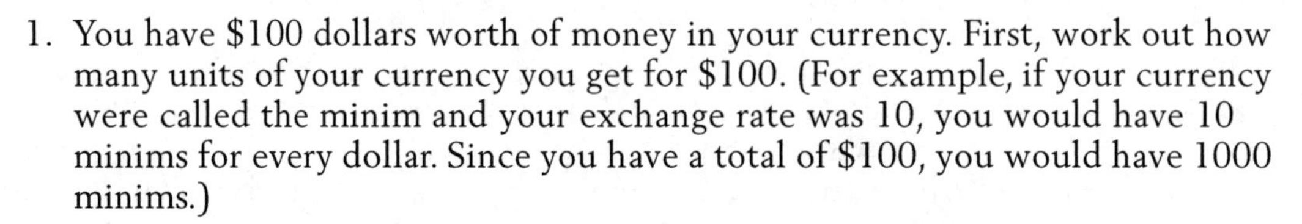

Your group will represent one of these countries.

1. You have $100 dollars worth of money in your currency. First, work out how many units of your currency you get for $100. (For example, if your currency were called the minim and your exchange rate was 10, you would have 10 minims for every dollar. Since you have a total of $100, you would have 1000 minims.)

2. Now you need to create some bank notes so that you can buy things with the money. Decide what denominations you need in your currency. Will ones, fives, and tens work for your currency? Or do you need to start with hundreds and thousands?

3. Design and create bank notes for your currency. Each note should show the name of your country, the name of your currency, and the value of each note—one, ten, one hundred, and so on.

(continued)

Name ______________________________ Date ______________________

Money in West Africa: Cedi, Dalasi, Naira *(continued)*

4. Now you need to create export cards for the items you export. The total value of your exports must equal the total value of your currency. Assign a value to each export card. (Again, let's suppose your currency is the minim and you export diamonds, gold, and peanuts. You have a total of 1000 minims. You might say that your diamonds were worth 500 minims, your gold was worth 400 minims, and your peanuts were worth 100 minims, for a total of 1000 minims.) Design and create cards for each item you export. Each card should show the name of the country, what the export is, and what the value of the item is.
5. Once you have money and things to export, it's time to get trading. Go to another group and make two exchanges with them. Buy one of their exports from them and sell them one of your exports. Convert your currency into their currency to make the sale. Don't worry if you can't match the currencies exactly because the units of your notes don't match; just get as close as you can.
6. Working in your group, write out the details of each transaction. Show your currency, the other group's currency, and how you converted from one currency to the other.

Bonus Question

Eight of the countries of West Africa use the same currency, the franc CFA, and have the same exchange rate. Why do you think this might be?

____

____

____

____

West African Folktales

Objectives

English/Language Arts

- Students will write their own version of a folktale.

Social Studies

- Students will understand that folktales can be used to transmit culture.
- Students will learn that West Africans consider honoring their ancestors important.

Materials

West African Folktales handout
paper and pencils
optional: Brer Rabbit and Anansi tales that tell similar stories—for example,"Brer Rabbit and the Tar Baby" and the Anansi story "How Stories Came to Earth"

Background

The story on the student page is a shortened version of a West African folktale. It introduces the concept of honoring one's ancestors. Many Africans believe that a person's ancestors continue to influence the world of their descendants. The ancestors may work for the good of their kinsmen, or they may cause illness or misfortune among them. For this reason, it is believed that those who die should be honored frequently, so that they will work to influence supernatural forces on behalf of the family and the community.

Procedure

1. Distribute the handout and discuss it with students. If you wish, read aloud a Brer Rabbit story and a similar story from West Africa. Ask students to think about why these stories might have gone so easily from the West African vernacular to the American one. Encourage them to see that many of the elements in the stories are universal. They address ideas common to many cultures.
2. Have students read the story "The Cow-Tail Switch." What elements in the story are distinctly African? (the hunt, the cow-tail switch) What elements are found in many cultures? (the idea that parents should be respected and honored)
3. Have students brainstorm some important elements in their culture. They can include elements that are a part of North American culture as a whole or elements that reflect a regional or local culture—even a school culture.

4. Divide the class into groups. Have each group choose one aspect of culture to write about. Students then proceed as directed on the handout.

Variation

Have students adapt "The Cow-Tail Switch" for an American listener, as the Brer Rabbit stories were adapted.

Assessment

Did students write a folktale that encapsulates some important aspect of the named culture?

Name ______________________________ Date ______________

West African Folktales

Have you ever heard or read a story about Brer Rabbit? He is a trickster figure who appears in a lot of American folktales. Most people don't know that Brer Rabbit came from Africa.

For several centuries Europeans, Americans, and Africans sold people from Africa as slaves. Many of these slaves came from West Africa. In fact, the area along the Gulf of Guinea came to be called the Slave Coast. Men, woman, and children were uprooted from their homes in Africa and forced to take a terrible trip across the Atlantic. Many of them died. Many more died from the hard work they had to do on the plantations in America.

Those who survived tried to keep their culture alive. It was something to hold on to in their strange new lives. Telling stories was an important part of West African culture. Many of the stories had some kind of moral or message. They were used to help pass on the ethics of their people, to transmit knowledge, and to bring an awareness of common values and virtues.

Many of the stories we know today as Brer Rabbit stories are almost exactly the same as the stories told by people in West Africa. The only changes are the names and the setting—from West Africa to rural America.

Here is another story told in West Africa.

The Cow-Tail Switch

A hunter named Ogaloussa once lived near the edge of the forest. He lived with his wife and many children. One morning Ogaloussa took his weapons and went into the forest to hunt. The day passed and darkness came, but Ogaloussa did not return. Another day went by, and then weeks. Still Ogaloussa did not come back from the forest.

At first Ogaloussa's sons often spoke of their father. As time passed they talked about him less. Eventually, they never even mentioned his name.

After he had been gone about four months, Ogaloussa's wife bore another son. The boy was given the name Puli.

When Puli was old enough to talk, his first words were, "Where is my father?"

The other sons, slightly surprised by the question, looked across the fields.

"Yes," asked one of them, as he now remembered his father. "Where is our father?"

"Something must have happened. We ought to look for him," said another.

So the sons took their weapons and set out to look for Ogaloussa. Several times in the deep forest, they lost the trail.But each time one of the sons would find it again. At last they came to a clearing. There on the ground lay Ogaloussa's bones and his rusty weapons. They knew then that Ogaloussa had been killed in the hunt.

(continued)

Name ______________________________ Date ______________

West African Folktales *(continued)*

One of the sons stepped forward."I know how to put a dead person's bones together." He gathered all of Ogaloussa's bones and put them together, each in its right place.

Another said, "I know how to cover the skeleton with sinews and flesh." He went to work and covered Ogaloussa's bones with sinews and flesh. A third son put blood into the body. A fourth added breath. Movement and speech were added by other sons. At last Ogaloussa sat up and spoke."Where are my weapons?" he asked. His sons picked up the rusted weapons and gave them to their father. Then they started home through the forest.

At home Ogaloussa bathed and ate and remained in the house for four days. On the fifth day he came out of the house. He killed a cow for a great feast. From the cow's tail he braided a switch. He decorated it with beads and shells and shiny metal. It was a beautiful thing. Everyone in the village admired the switch. They thought it was the most beautiful cow-tail switch they had ever seen.

A celebration was arranged in the village because Ogaloussa had returned from the dead. At the celebration, some of the men grew bold and asked for the switch. Then all the women and children begged for it. Ogaloussa refused them all. At last Ogaloussa stood up, and the noise stopped, for everyone wanted to hear what he had to say.

"While I was hunting," he began, "I was killed by a leopard. My sons brought me back from the land of the dead, and it is one of them who must receive the switch. Though all my sons did something to bring me back, I have only one cow-tail switch. I will give it to the one who did the most to bring me home."

The sons began to argue. One claimed that he had done the most because he had found the trail when it was lost. Another said he should have the switch because he had put the bones together. Still another deserved it, he said, because he had put blood into Ogaloussa's body. Each son claimed the right to possess the wonderful cow-tail switch.

The villagers began to choose sides, arguing for the son they thought had done the most to bring Ogaloussa back from the land of the dead. They argued back and forth until Ogaloussa asked them to be quiet. He came forward and bent low and handed it to Puli, the little boy who had been born while Ogaloussa was in the forest.

"To this son I will give the cow-tail switch, for I owe most to him," Ogaloussa said.

The people of the village remembered then that the child's first words had been, "Where is my father?" They knew that Ogaloussa was right. For it was a saying among them that a man is not really dead until he is forgotten.

(continued)

Name ______________________ Date ______________

West Africa Folktales *(continued)*

Remember that West Africans used stories to keep their culture alive, to pass on wisdom and knowledge.The stories always have a message. They are told to remind people of important virtues in the culture. What do you think is the message in this story? What can it teach you about traditional culture in West Africa? Does this story relate to anything in your culture?

In your group, discuss some of the important ideas in your culture. Perhaps you feel that hard work is an important part of your culture or religious faith. What about honesty or courage?

Choose one important part of your culture. Then develop an original folktale that shows how important this idea is. If you wish, you can illustrate your story. Choose a member from your group to read the story to the class.

Story Title: ______________________

Important Idea: ______________________

____

____

Plot: ______________________

____

____

____

____

Music of West Africa

Objectives

Music

- Students will understand the importance of traditional African instruments.
- Students will explore the various rhythms that can be made with the drum.
- Students will make their own simple musical instruments.

Social Studies

- Students will understand how music contributes to the development and transmission of culture.
- Students will compare the ways in which different groups of people address the same concerns.
- Students will see that culture is an integrated whole and that language, literature, the arts, traditions, beliefs, and values all interact to form it.

Materials for Drumsticks (for drum and xylophone)

ruler
two dowels about 12" long
two large beads or small balls with a dowel-sized hole drilled in each of them

Materials for Drum

Drum handout
two drumsticks
nail or paper punch
cord or rawhide lacing
ruler or tape measure
large empty can (coffee can works well) with both ends removed
glue
pencil
scissors
chamois
rubber bands

Materials for Xylophone

Xylophone handout
saw or utility knife
scissors
piece of cardboard or wood 8" × $14\frac{1}{2}$"
glue
ruler
pencil
two drumsticks

Materials for Xylophone *continued*

one piece of 7/8" × 7/8" wood in each of the following lengths:
12 1/8", 11 1/2", 10 3/4", 10 1/4", 9 5/8", 8 1/2", 8 3/8"

two strips of 1/2" wide felt, one 14 1/2" long, one 15" long
(felt weather-stripping works well)

optional: drill, 1/8" diameter dowel

Materials for Flute

Flute handout
utility knife
drill
ruler
cork
length of bamboo or plastic pipe 11 1/2" long and 3/4" or 7/8" in diameter

Materials for Zither

Zither handout
16 small nails
16 screw eyes
piece of wood 1" × 11" × 16"
guitar string or nylon monofilament
saw
ruler
pencil
hammer

Variation for Zither

For a better-sounding instrument, make a simple wooden box 11 × 16 × 8, with a 3" hole in the center of the top of the box. Cut two strips of 1/2" × 1/2" wood, one 11" long, one 13 1/2" long. Attach the 11" strip to the lower end of the box and the 13 1/2" strip along the angled edge. Proceed as for the board zither.

Background

Music and dance are important throughout Africa. The instruments used can be divided into four groups: idiophones, membranophones, aerophones, and chordophones.

Idiophones are instruments that produce sound without the addition of a stretched membrane or a vibrating reed or string. Rhythm idiophones include rattles, gongs, cymbals, finger bells, and wooden drums made by carving slits in one side of a hollowed-out log. Idiophones used to play melodies—tuned idiophones—include the xylophone and the *mbira* or *sansa*, which consists of a graduated series of wooden or metal keys mounted on a resonator.

Membranophones, drums with parchment heads, are very important in African music. They can be as simple as a skin apron stretched over pots, or they can be carefully constructed and elaborately decorated. Each society usually specializes in a small number of drum types.

African music uses only a few aerophones, or wind instruments. They include flutes, reed pipes, horns, and trumpets.

The last grouping, chordophones, uses a vibrating string to create sound. The simplest chordophone is the earth bow. This consists of a flexible stick, stuck in the ground, with a piece of string attached to its upper end. The string is stretched down and buried in the earth; when it is plucked, the sound seems to be coming from the earth itself. Other chordophones include the mouth bow, bows with calabash resonators, zithers, lutes, and harps. Lyres, instruments whose strings run from a yoke to a resonator, are found mainly in eastern Africa.

The handouts in this section give directions for making an idiophone (xylophone), aerophone (flute), chordophone (zither), and membranophone (drum). Paul Berliner's book *Soul of Mbira* gives instructions for making an mbira, and mbira kits are available from a variety of sources.

Preparation

You may want all students to make the same instrument, or you may want to divide class into groups and have each group make a different instrument. If desired, cut the wooden base for the zither in advance.

Procedure

1. Distribute the Music of West Africa handout and discuss it with students. Remind students that jazz and rock were both heavily influenced by the music of West Africa. If possible, listen to a recording of West African music of today.
2. Distribute the directions for making instruments. Students proceed as directed on the handouts.

Variation

Students work in small groups to produce one main instrument per group, then collaborate to produce *ishakas*, or rattles, for all students. To make an ishaka, cut a length of plastic piping or cardboard tubing (paper towel tube, mailing tube). Cover one end with a circle of paper and tape securely in place. Put a handful of beans or rice inside the tube. Cover the other end with paper and tape. If desired, decorate the outside of the tube. To play, just shake. Experiment with different length tubes and different amounts of materials inside the tube to create different sounds. When all instruments are completed, gather your ensemble together and play!

Assessment

Did students make working versions of West African instruments?

Name ______________________ Date ______________

Music of West Africa

From the Middle Ages on, European music developed its own distinct pattern. Music was defined in the West as a pleasing arrangement of sounds. Although it was sometimes combined with other activities, like dancing, music was usually a separate activity. You stopped whatever else you were doing and listened to it.

Traditional African music is not just for listening. It is always part of something else. In fact, you could say that music is part of everything else in Africa. Almost all events in West African life—social and daily events, the harvest, funerals, baptisms, rituals—include music. Sometimes the music accompanies a song or a story. Sometimes it accompanies a dance. Always, the rhythm is important. An Ewe proverb says, "How the drum beats determines the way you move your feet."

People who have learned to appreciate music from the Western point of view may find the music of Africa hard to understand. Instead of concentrating on harmony, African music concentrates on rhythm. Instead of the even beat of Western music, African music can have several different beats, one on top of the other. The music that results is rich and complex. To listeners accustomed to the steady beat of Western music, it can sound either energetic or disorganized.

Drums are among the best-known African instruments. When we think of rhythm, we think of the beat of a drum. But drums aren't the only instruments made and played in West Africa. *Griots*, or storytellers, use a kind of harp, the *kora*, to accompany their words. The *mbira*, an instrument with a sounding box and wooden or metal keys, comes in many forms. It can have as few as 5 keys, or as many as 45. Xylophones, with wooden keys, can be played as solo instruments or in small groups. And wind instruments—flutes, pipes, horns, and trumpets—are widely used.

In West Africa today, traditional music is still very important. But music like *juju* and Afro-beat are also popular. Popular music in West Africa often uses Western instruments as well as African ones and combines traditional African music with jazz and rock. Since jazz and rock were both influenced by the ethnic music of African Americans, this new music could be described as traditional music that has traveled in a big circle, from Africa to America and back. And as juju and Afro-beat music by performers like King Sunny Ade and Fela Anikulapo-Kuti become more popular in the West, that circular effect keeps on going.

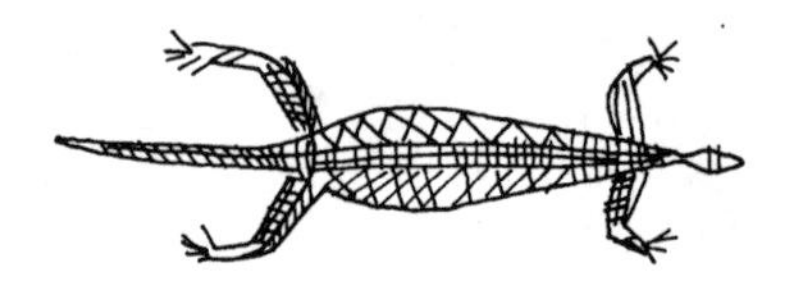

(continued)

Name ______________________________ Date ______________

Music of West Africa *(continued)*

Drum

In traditional African societies, the drum was more than a musical instrument. It was an important communication tool. You could almost say it filled the role the telephone fills in modern society.

Even today, drums are more than just a way of setting the rhythm for music. There are many different kinds of drums for different purposes and for different kinds of drumming. One rhythm might be used to celebrate a birth, another a death, a wedding, and so forth. Learning to play the drum well takes years of practice. Master drummers are respected in the community.

Most drums are made of wood and animal skins, but gourds, calabashes, and earthenware pots are also used. Toy drums for children are sometimes made from old tin cans. Follow the steps below to make your own drum.

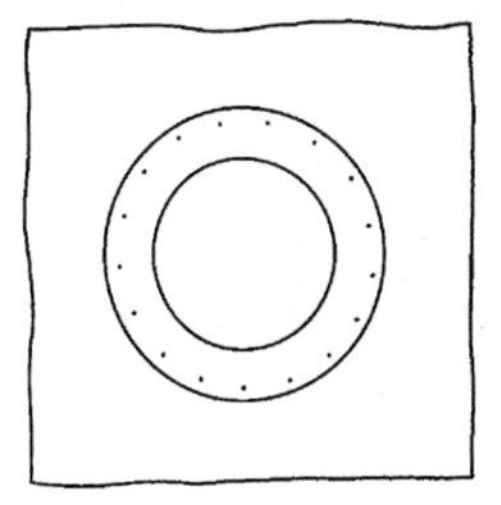

1. Use the end of the can to trace two circles on the chamois, at least 4" apart. Now draw circles 2" outside and around the first two circles. Cut out along the outer lines.
2. Use the nail or a paper punch to make holes every 2" about ½" from the edge of the chamois circles.
3. Put the pieces of chamois in a basin of cold water and let them soak for 20 minutes.
4. Squeeze the extra water out of the chamois, then place one circle over each end of the coffee can. Hold the chamois in place with rubber bands.
5. Lace the two circles together by threading the cord or rawhide through the punched holes. Then set it aside to dry. As the chamois dries, it will shrink, creating a taut drumhead.

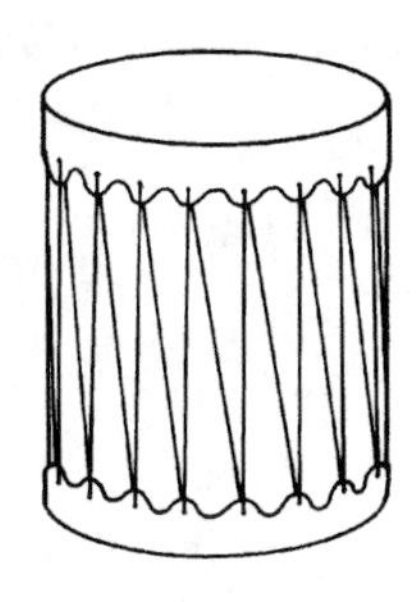

To make drumsticks, glue a bead or ball onto one end of each dowel. You're ready to drum!

(continued)

Name ____________________ Date ____________________

Music of West Africa *(continued)*

Xylophone

Xylophones (known as *balafons*) are widely used in West Africa. The simplest type of xylophone is the leg xylophone. The musician sits, legs outstretched, and places three or four wooden bars crosswise from one leg to the other. The leg xylophone is played by hitting the bars with a mallet or stick.

The frame xylophone is also popular. The keys—pieces of wood of different lengths—are mounted in a wooden frame. Dried gourds are mounted under the keys to make the sound more resonant.

Another type of xylophone is also common in West Africa. It is easy to put together and take apart, and it can be as large or as small as desired. Two banana-tree trunks are laid on the ground, not quite parallel. At one end they are quite close together but at the other end they are farther apart. The keys of the xylophone are slabs of wood of different lengths. The shortest slabs are placed across the logs where they are closest together, and the longest slabs go at the other end where the logs are farther apart. They are kept in position by sticks attached to the banana tree between the keys. The log xylophone is often played by two musicians at once.

In this activity, you will make a small version of this type of xylophone. Instead of logs, you will use strips of felt as supports, and blocks of wood for keys.

1. To assemble the xyophone frame, place the wood or cardboard base so that its long edges are at the top and bottom and its short edges are the sides. On the left edge, measure $4\frac{3}{8}$" up from the bottom and make a mark. Draw a straight line from the mark to the upper right corner of the base. Cut along this line.

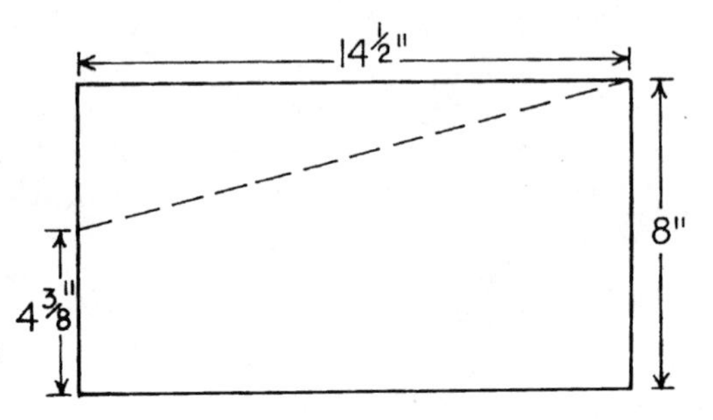

(continued)

Name ______________________________ Date ______________

Music of West Africa *(continued)*

Xylophone

2. Glue the shorter strip of felt along the bottom edge of the base. Glue the longer felt strip along the edge of the angled cut you made.

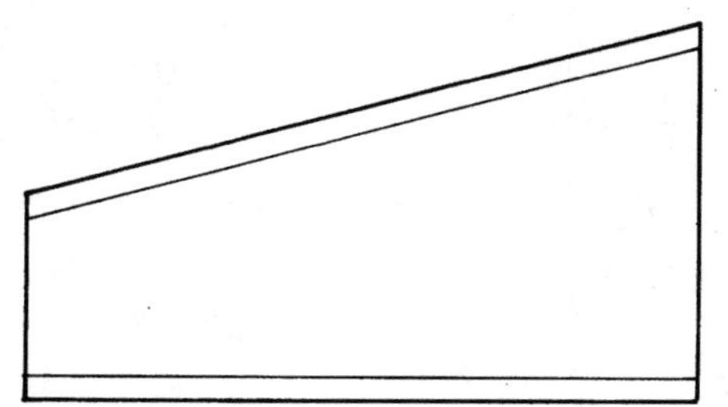

3. To assemble the xylophone, start by placing the shortest block of wood across the frame about 2" in from the left edge. It should overlap at both ends.
4. Leaving $\frac{1}{2}$" between blocks, arrange the rest of the blocks on the frame. If you wish, drill holes in the frame and insert short lengths of dowels between the blocks to keep them from shifting.

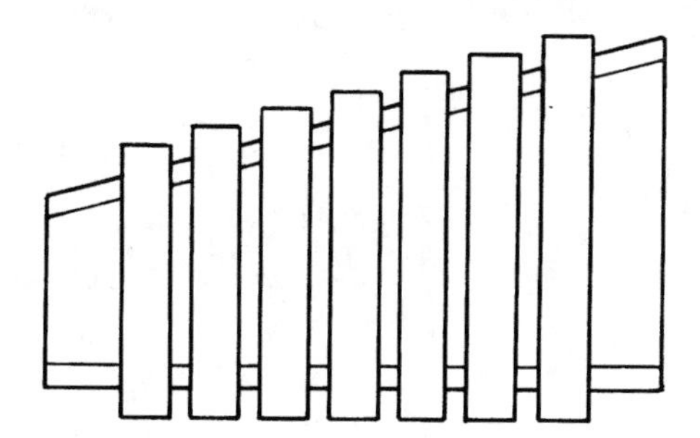

5. To make drumsticks, glue a wooden bead or ball onto one end of each 12" dowel. Play the xylophone by striking the blocks of wood in the center with the drumsticks.

(continued)

Name ______________________________ Date ______________

Music of West Africa *(continued)*

Bamboo Flute

Many kinds of wind instruments are played in West Africa: horns, trumpets, clarinets, oboes, whistles, and flutes. Flutes may be carved out of wood, or they may be made from something that is naturally hollow. Hollow materials include bamboo, cane husks, and millet stalks.

In this activity, you will make a simple flute from bamboo or plastic piping.

1. Use a drill to make holes in the tube. Don't forget to include the thumb hole at the back.

thumb hole at back →

2. Shape the mouthpiece.

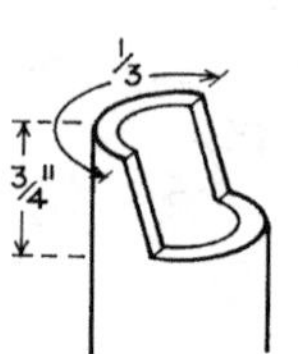

3. Cut a channel in the mouthpiece.

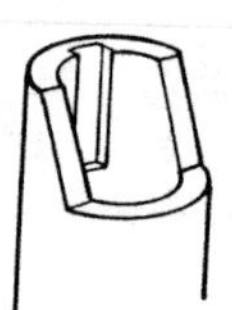

4. Cut the cork.

5. Insert the cork in the mouthpiece.

To play, blow gently into the mouthpiece. Covering the holes with your fingers and thumb will give different notes.

(continued)

Name ______________________ Date ______________

Music of West Africa *(continued)*

Board Zither

Some stringed instruments are played by running a bow across their strings. Some are played by plucking the individual strings. Zithers fall into this second group of instruments.

In this activity you will make a simple version of a zither.

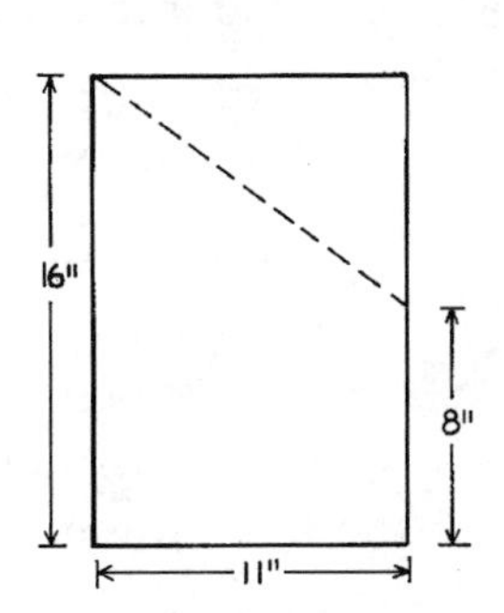

1. Place the board so that its long edges are at the sides and its short edges are at the top and bottom. Measure 8" up from the bottom on the right-hand side. Make a mark. Draw a straight line from the mark to the upper left corner of the wood. Cut the wood along this line.

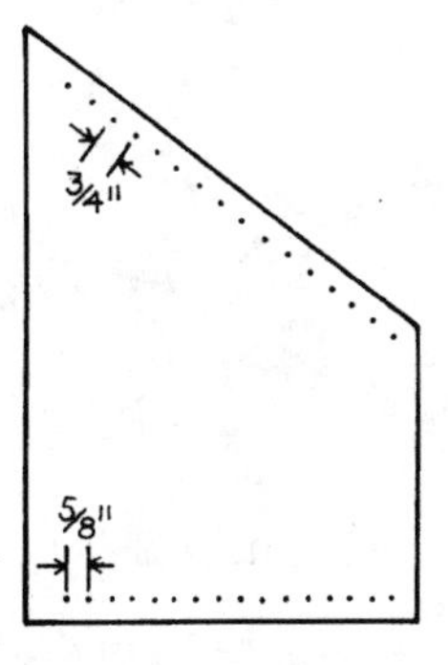

2. Starting 1" in from the left side, mark 16 dots along the lower edge, 5/8" apart.
3. Starting 1" in from the left side, mark 16 dots along the angled edge, 3/4" apart.
4. Hammer small nails partway into the board at the dots along the lower edge. About 1/4" of the nails should stick out of the wood.
5. Screw the eye fasteners partway into the angled edge at the pencil marks. They should be firmly attached but not screwed all the way in.

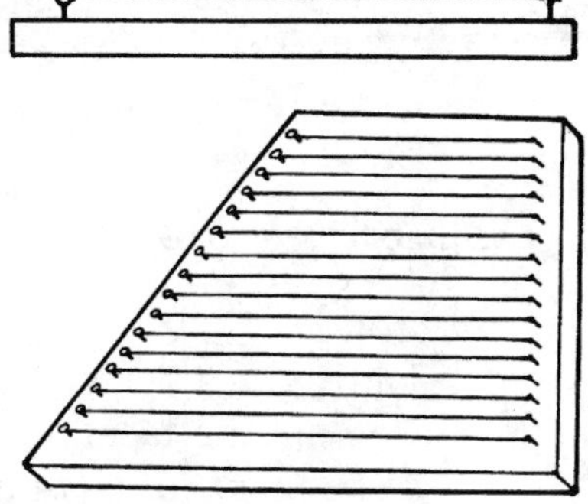

6. To string the zither, tie a length of nylon monofilament (or other line) to the nail at the far left. Run the line along the face of the zither to the screw eye at the far left. Wrap the line two or three times around the neck of the eye, then tie it to the eye itself.
7. Repeat step 6 for the remaining nails and screw eyes, using a separate length of line for each one.
8. Tune the zither by turning the screw eyes to tighten or loosen each string. Play by plucking the strings with fingers or with a pick.

Benin: Appliqué Art of Dahomey

Objectives

Social Studies

- Students will understand that information about a region is not limited to written sources.
- Students will understand that art can provide a way of communicating and preserving historical events.
- Students will understand that art can help preserve the traditions and customs of a culture.

Art

- Students will understand some of the ways in which the history of a society affects its artistic development.
- Students will experiment with creating visual symbols for communication.
- Students will understand that art often uses symbols unique to the culture in which it is created.

Materials

The Art of Dahomey handout
paper
pencils
scissors
markers

For paper appliqué

glue sticks
construction paper in a variety of colors
poster board in black or dark blue for background

or

For fabric appliqué

iron
fabric glue
iron-on interfacing
small pieces of cloth in a variety of colors
large pieces of black or dark fabric for background

Group Size

Although this project can be successfully performed by individuals, it is also an excellent cooperative activity, as it encourages finding group consensus on the meaning of symbols. Groups of three to five students work well.

Background

The kingdom of Dahomey was founded in the early seventeenth century in the area that is now called Benin. Over the centuries it became a powerful kingdom, despite conflict with other states and the increasing European presence in the area. In 1708 Agadja became king and increased the strength of Dahomey by creating a military training school and a corps of women soldiers. Dahomey continued to prosper until 1894, when it became a colony under French rule.

Throughout the history of Dahomey, art has played an important role. Several arts, including working brass and making appliqué cloth, could only be practiced by the king's retainers. The appliqué artists were organized into family guilds who held the monopoly for making the cloth. Their work was used to show the importance and prestige of the king and of the people he appointed to official positions.

The hangings of Dahomey were usually done on a black or gold background, using small pieces of colored fabric to create a design. Hangings were made to commemorate victories in battle or successful hunts. Appliqué banners were carried at funerals. Pillows were decorated with the symbols of royalty or with religious or political insignia. Religious and military associations had appliqué cloth banners with symbols relating to their societies.

The symbols used in these banners and hangings had multiple meanings and were often associated with proverbs. For example, the symbol of one past king of Dahomey is a fish near a trap. One saying that goes with this symbol is "The fish who escapes the trap does not return"—or as we might say, "Once bitten, twice shy."

Preparation

This activity can be done with fabric or with colored paper. The fabric gives a more authentic product but the paper is easier to use. However, even with the fabric method, there are short cuts to make the process easier. Instead of turning under the edge of the cloth to prevent fraying, use iron-on interfacing. Following the manufacturer's directions, attach the interfacing to the *wrong* side of the fabric to be used as appliqué motifs. Students can then simply cut out the motifs and attach them to the background. (You do not need to do this on the fabric to be used as a background.) Another shortcut is to use a fabric adhesive, rather than sewing, to attach the appliqué motifs to the background. Various products, from glue to iron-on adhesive, are available. Choose the one that suits you best, and follow the manufacturer's directions for use.

Procedure

1. Distribute the handout and discuss it with students. Make sure that students understand the way symbols were used for communication. Lead them to see

that visual symbols can be used in the same way as verbal symbols, like the letters we use to form words. For example, Glele was a powerful king of Dahomey. We agree that the letters "G-l-e-l-e" can be used to symbolize the king. In the same way, the people of Dahomey agreed that a lion could be used to symbolize King Glele. Whenever a lion appears on a banner, it is equivalent to writing the word *Glele*. Encourage students to think of symbols widely accepted in our culture, like road signs, the American eagle, and so forth.

2. As a class, brainstorm to find symbols for some general aspects of our culture. What symbol could you use for the country as a whole? for the government? for the president? for your state, your school, a school sports team, the school principal? Agree on symbols for some general subjects like these.

3. If you wish, divide students into groups. Students proceed as directed on the handout to choose a story to tell and to develop a design. If you wish, you can choose a general theme for the banners—perhaps a specific event in West African history—and direct students to choose stories that fall under that general heading.

4. Distribute materials and tell students how to proceed. If using paper, they should transfer their designs to the colored paper, cut out the motifs, and attach them to the background sheet with glue sticks. If using fabric, students should use markers to transfer their design to the colored fabric and then cut out the motifs and attach them to the background, using fabric glue. With either method, final details can be added with markers.

Assessment

Mount the students' banners on the wall. Have other groups try to guess what story each banner is telling. If the rest of the class can "read" at least part of the story, the banner is successful.

Name ______________________________ Date ______________

Benin: Appliqué Art of Dahomey

Well into the fifteenth century, the only printed books in the world were made in China and Japan. Everywhere else stories and ideas could only be preserved in a few ways. They could be written out by hand in a book, one book at a time. They could be memorized and told by one person to another. Or they could be told through art.

The oral tradition—one person memorizing a story and telling it to another person—is important in West Africa. But many cultures also developed visual ways to tell their stories. The Dahomey culture of Benin was one of these. The artists of Dahomey developed a type of cloth hanging that told a story. Some hangings told of an event in history. Some were used to trace the kings of the area. All of them used a technique we call appliqué.

The word appliqué comes from the French word for "applied." To make a piece of appliqué, the artist cut small shapes from fabric and applied them to a larger piece of cloth. The appliqué artists of Dahomey worked for the king. They used this technique to make beautiful hangings and banners.

To make sure other people could understand the stories, the artists of Dahomey used symbols. For example, a king named Agadja ruled Dahomey from 1708 to 1740. Because he was the first king of Dahomey to deal with Europeans, a sailing ship was used as his symbol. Another king was shown as a fish near a trap. Other symbols were a boar and a lion.

Dahomey-style hangings can be used to tell all kinds of stories. They may tell the history of an area, a story from a family's history, the highlights of a sports event, or the outcome of a political race.

Think of a story you would like to tell in an appliqué hanging. Decide how you will show different people and events and what symbols you will use. Work out the design on a piece of paper. Then follow your teacher's directions to complete the hanging.

> Yoruba is one of the languages spoken in Benin.
> "Hello" in Yoruba is *bawoni.*
> "Good-bye" is *odabo.*

Burkina Faso: Building a House

Objectives

Science

- Students will understand some of the insulating properties of mud as a building material.

Math

- Students will construct a model building, using geometric shapes.

Social Studies

- Students will compare the similarities and differences in the ways different cultures construct housing.

Geography

- Students will understand how buildings are shaped by the environment.

Art

- Students will use the coil method to build a clay cylinder.
- Students will experiment with applying geometric decorations to a curved surface.

Materials

Building a House handout
self-hardening clay
ruler
pencil
craft sticks and other utensils to work clay
one 8" square of firm cardboard for each student
acrylic or tempera paints in earth colors: black, white, sienna, ochre, tan, and others

Background

Traditionally, cylindrical houses were found in many parts of Africa. One advantage of using a circle as a base is that a circle of a given perimeter encloses more area than a square or a rectangle of the same perimeter. Thus, a round house encloses more space with the same amount of wall building.

Mud and clay are used in most of West Africa as building materials. The clay is usually formed into bricks and dried in the sun to make adobe. As a building material, mud is not very durable. It tends to crack at high temperatures and to erode in the downpours of West Africa's rainy season. Still, it has a lot of advantages. It is easily available, easy to work with and repair, and it can be ornamented in a variety of ways.

It is also a practical building material for keeping a house cool in hot weather. During the day, as the sun beats down on the mud, it slowly absorbs heat but transmits very little to the interior of the house. At night, when the outside air cools down, the warm adobe gradually loses its heat to the cooler air. The interior of the house maintains a fairly even temperature.

In one study of adobe houses and temperature variation, temperature readings were taken inside and outside a house at two-hour intervals. At 6:00 A.M. both interior and exterior readings were 71° F. At noon the outside reading was 102° F; inside, it was 79° F. At 2:00 P.M. the outside temperature had reached 105° F while the inside air was still only 80° F. At 10:00 P.M. the temperature outside had dropped to 75° F. The temperature inside had risen to 84° F. The temperature variation outside the building was 34° F. Inside, it was 13° F (Lumpkin and Strong, *Multicultural Science and Math Connections*).

While mud is used throughout West Africa, building style varies from place to place, as does the method of house decoration. The illustration on page 28 shows a compound belonging to a Nankani family in Burkina Faso. Mural paintings like this are no longer common in Burkina Faso, but some families maintain the tradition. Houses are usually painted by women, using pigments made from different types of earth and ground limestone.

In Burkina Faso, every compound is different, because each family builds to meet its own specific needs, and according to their resources. Each compound includes dwellings for living and sleeping, covered storage areas, and dry and wet season kitchens. The dwellings have a flat earthen roof, used for food drying and storage and as a cooler sleeping area in very hot weather. Storage buildings and other outbuildings usually have conical thatched roofs.

The compound also includes a corral for animals like goats and chickens. A low wall separates the corral from the living area; a stepping-stone, or stile, makes crossing the wall easier. Ladders, often made of notched tree trunks, give access to the rooftop areas. The separate grain storage areas are often built on wooden stilts, offering both increased ventilation and protection from rodents. The raised buildings also provide welcome shade for the chickens often kept on the ground below.

Even in rural areas, compounds like this are being affected by the availability of industrial materials. Concrete blocks and corrugated metal are increasingly replacing adobe as building materials.

Procedure

1. Distribute the handout and discuss it with students. Point out that it is easy to draw a small circle on cardboard by using a compass. How would students draw a large circle on the ground to be used as the shape of a house? Encourage students to come up with ways to draw a large circle using simple tools, like a length of rope attached to an upright stick.
2. Students proceed as directed on the handout.

Variations

- Form students into groups of four or five. When students have finished their individual houses, have them group their houses into compounds. All the houses should face onto a central courtyard. They can be connected with low walls and animal pens. A taller outer wall, with a gate or other opening, should surround the whole compound.
- Many different kinds of housing are to be found in West Africa. In the cities, buildings look very much like buildings in western cities. In some wet areas, like the Lake Nohoui area of Benin, houses are built on stilts to keep them above the level of the water. Have groups of students each research a different housing type, and build a model house. Display to show the variety of West African architecture.

Bonus Question

Ask students which they think has more space inside, a round house with a perimeter of 44 feet, or a square house with the same perimeter? (*Hint*: The diameter of the round house will be 14' and the sides of the square will be 11', based on a perimeter of 44'.)

The round house is bigger. The total area of the circle is $22/7 \times 7^2$ or 154 square feet. The area of the square house is 11^2 or 121 square feet.

Assessment

Did students build a cylindrical structure as directed and decorate it using geometric motifs?

Moore is one of the languages spoken in Burkina Faso.

How are you?	Kebara	(kee-bar-*ray*)
Good-bye	Win na kond yindara	(win na kond yin-*dah*-ray)
Yes	Onhow	(ong-hong)
No	Ononk	(hon-hon)
Thank you	Barka	(*bah*-kah)

Name ______________________ Date ______________

Burkino Faso: Building a House

The houses we live in are one aspect of culture. When the first Europeans came to West Africa, they brought their own culture with them. In Europe, the climate was cool, and wood and stone were easy to find. Europeans built houses to keep the cold out and the heat in. Most family activities, especially in winter, took place indoors.

Because of this, the Europeans found houses in places like Burkina Faso hard to accept. Many traditional houses there were built of mud or clay, with thick walls. They were cylinders, not rectangles, and they had very few windows. The doors were usually low arches. Mud was even used for furniture: sitting platforms, beds, and shelving were all part of the building itself, formed out of mud. Europeans saw these houses as "poor" and "primitive."

In fact, these houses are a creative response to climate and available building materials. They combine comfort, usefulness, and pleasing appearance. Although mud is not a very durable building material, it is a very practical one. Unlike wood and stone, mud is easy to get in most parts of Burkina Faso. You don't need special tools, like saws and hammers and chisels, to build with mud. You can make round buildings or square buildings or buildings in any shape you please. You can build the mud up to form "built-ins," like beds and benches and cupboards. And mud has another important feature that makes it well-suited for building in a hot climate. It absorbs heat during the day, and slowly releases it at night. This means that the inside of a building made of mud will stay cool during the day.

Traditionally, West African families don't live all together in one house. They build a small house for each family member and group all the houses together inside an outer wall. This grouping of houses is called a compound.

Inside the compound, the individual houses are often connected with low walls. These walls can be used to form pens for animals. The separate buildings form one harmonious unit.

This harmony is often increased by decorating the outside of the houses. Painting styles and designs vary from place to place, but they all use natural pigments made from clay and earth, and most designs are based on geometric forms.

Traditional houses are still seen in the country, but in cities, people live in houses and apartments very much like buildings in other cities around the world. Even in the country, it is not uncommon to see a house of wood or marble side-by-side with a mud house!

1. Use the coil method to build a house out of clay. Roll the clay between your hands to form several long, even rolls. Try not to let the rolls get thin in some parts and thick in others, as this will make your walls hard to build.

(continued)

Name ______________________ Date ______________

Burkino Faso: Building a House *(continued)*

2. Draw a circle on the cardboard base. Use this as a template for the base of your house. Place your clay roll on the circle, pressing lightly when you come to the end of the ring. Keep going, running the roll of clay along the top of the first circle. The second circle should be right on top of the first. If it hangs over a bit at the front or back, or leans in one direction, your finished walls will be crooked.

3. Continue building up the walls of your house with clay. As you finish one roll of clay, add another one, squeezing the ends together. Stop when the walls are about 6" high.

4. Using your fingers, a spoon, or a craft stick, smooth the surface of the clay, inside and outside, to blend the separate coils of clay together. The walls should look like a single surface.Cut a low arched doorway in one side of your house. Cut one or two small windows, either round or square, for ventilation.

5. Cut a low arched doorway in one side of your house. Cut one or two small windows, either round or square, for ventilation.

6. To form a flat roof, make a ledge on the inside of the walls, about 2" down from the top. Use coils or a slab of clay to make a circle the same diameter as your house. Carefully lower the circle of clay onto the inside ledge. Smooth all joints and edges carefully. Set your house aside to dry.

7. Use natural earth colors to decorate your house. Most of your designs should be combinations of geometric shapes. You can use the drawing on this page for ideas.

Côte d'Ivoire: Baule Gold Plating

Objectives

Social Studies

- Students will understand how art and artifacts can contribute to culture.

Art

- Students will create a carved plaque and coat it with foil.
- Students will understand that art is connected to culture and history.

Materials

Baule Gold Plating handout
gold or silver foil
self-hardening clay
toothpicks and other instruments for carving
optional: jewelry findings, like pin backs or pendant rings
glue
ruler or tape measure

Background

The Baule people of the Côte d'Ivoire originally lived in Ghana. As the story on the student page relates, they emigrated westward some 300 years ago. Although other peoples also use gold plating to cover wooden objects, Baule gold plating is unique because it is so densely patterned. Usually, the entire surface of the wood is carved before being covered with gold. An item may have one central motif, but the entire background is usually covered with a network of interlocking lines and shapes.

To make gold leaf, the metalworker starts with gold dust. The dust is melted in a crucible to form a lump about the size of a pea. This lump is hammered on the anvil until it forms a sheet of gold about 0.05 mm thick, and about 3" × 4" in area.

The carved wooden object is coated in glue and the gold plate is applied in strips. It is carefully pressed into all the indentations in the wood using the fingers and small smooth tools made of bone.

Although the gold is thus firmly attached to the wood, gold-plated objects are treated very carefully. The gilded parts of the objects are not touched, and they are carefully wrapped in cotton when not in use.

Procedure

Distribute the handout and go over it with the students. Students proceed as directed on the handout.

Assessment

Did students carve a clay plaque and coat it in foil?

Name ______________________ Date ______________

Côte d'Ivoire: Baule Gold Plating

According to legend, the Baule people originally lived in Ghana. Their queen, Abraha-Pokou, was famous for her wisdom. In a time of good harvests, she told her people to put by a portion of their grain in case poor harvests came. When famine struck, the Baule had food. But other peoples attacked them for the grain. To save their food, Queen Abraha-Pokou led her people west from Ghana to the Côte d'Ivoire, where they live today.

The Baule came from an area where objects were made of gold and brass. In their new home, the people had a tradition of woodcarving. The Baule combined these two arts to form one of their own: covering carved wooden objects with a thin layer of gold. Gold-plated objects became symbols of leadership. For important occasions a Baule notable would carry a fly whisk with a carved, gold-plated wooden handle and would wear a black cloth hat on which small pieces of gold-plated wood were sewn. Some of these gold-plated plaques were plain, and others were carved with a human face or the figure of an animal before being covered in gold.

1. To make your own version of a Baule plaque, roll out some self-hardening clay until it is about $\frac{1}{4}$" thick. Cut a 2" square out of the clay.
2. Using the illustrations on this page for ideas, carve a design on your plaque. Set it aside to dry.
3. When your plaque is dry, you are ready to cover it in foil. Cut a piece of foil 3" × 3". Cover the plaque with a thin layer of glue. Lightly place the foil over the plaque. Starting at one corner, press the foil down onto the carving, making sure it goes into all the indentations. Use your fingers as much as possible. Where necessary, use the flat tip of a toothpick. Be careful; the foil tears easily.
4. When the entire plaque is covered with foil, turn it over. Spread glue on the outer $\frac{1}{2}$" of the back. Fold the overlapping areas of foil over from the front, and press down carefully.
5. If you wish, glue a pin backing or other finding on your plaque. Like the Baule, you can wear it in your hat!

Ghana: Kente Cloth

Objectives

Social Studies

- Students will

Art

- Students will make a simple loom and weave fabric according to specific criteria.

Math

- Students will create patterns based on triangles and rectangles.

Materials

Kente Cloth handout
ruler
pencil
scissors
utility knife
masking tape
tapestry needle
5" × 8" rectangle of firm card such as picture matting board
  or ready-made cardboard loom
kitchen string or crochet cotton for warp threads
embroidery floss or other thread or yarn for weft threads
optional: photographs or examples of kente cloth

Note: While any thread or yarn can be used for the weft threads, cotton embroidery floss, with its pearlized finish, probably comes closest to replicating the sheen of the original fabric. Rather than separating the floss into strands as they would for embroidery, students should use the entire strand. The thicker thread makes the work go more quickly.

Background

Kente cloth is a kind of weaving done by Asante men of Ghana. A narrow horizontal loom is used to weave long strips about 4" wide. Woven of cotton and silk, the cloth is often predominantly gold, with accents of red, blue, and green. Black and white are also used, but are less common.

At its most basic, weaving is very simple: Stretch a number of threads in one direction, and then at right angles to them, run another thread over and under every other one. Even stripes aren't that difficult. Just attach a new color at one edge of the work and weave with that color for a while. But the patterns in kente cloth aren't just stripes and solids. Rectangles are formed from triangles. Dramatic zigzags streak along the fabric. There are bands of pinwheels and diamond-shaped lozenges. Weaving these patterns means keeping track of several colors at once in both the weft and the warp—the vertical and horizontal threads. Kente cloth adds an additional challenge. Since the finished cloth is created by sewing together a number of narrow strips of fabric, the weaver must be able to visualize the whole while working on only one part.

In this activity, students will attempt weaving at its simplest. Still, even this should give them some idea of the challenges of weaving kente cloth. If nothing else, students are often impressed by how long it takes to weave even a few inches of cloth. If students try to incorporate curves, angles, or even boxes into their designs, they should understand some of the many calculations the weaver must make at all times.

If you wish, you can point out to students the relationship of the theme in the Bonwire story with that of the myth of Arachne. She was a Greek girl whose weaving was incomparable. Vain of her skill, she challenged the goddess Athena to a weaving competition. Angered by Arachne's boasting, Athena turned the girl into a spider—still a peerless weaver, but no longer able to boast about it.

Preparation

If you do not wish students to use a utility knife, prepare the looms in advance, as directed on the handout, or buy inexpensive cardboard looms, available through art suppliers.

Procedure

Distribute the handout and discuss it with students. Students proceed as directed on the handout. If you wish, when all students have finished their individual weavings, they can sew the strips together to form a larger cloth, as the weavers of kente cloth do.

Variation

Instead of weaving fabric, have students create kente designs with colored pencils on graph paper. Each horizontal square represents one warp thread, each vertical square a weft thread. Students try to create kente patterns by coloring in the squares.

Assessment

Did students weave a strip of cloth in the manner of kente cloth?

Name ______________________ Date ______________

Ghana: Kente Cloth

A long time ago, two men lived in Bonwire, a town in Ghana. One day, they saw a spider weaving its web. They watched it for a long time, seeing how individual threads were added. When the web was finished, it was a beautiful thing, made up of different geometric shapes. The men wondered if they could make cloth in the same way. They told no one what they were doing until they had finished a piece of cloth. The geometrical patterns recalled the spider's web, and the threads glistened like spider silk. The weavers showed their cloth to Nana Bobie, the chief of Bonwire. Nana Bobie showed the cloth to the Asantehene, or king. The Asantehene was pleased. He told the two men to weave him more cloth. Since then, weaving has been the most important work in Bonwire.

This story is told in Ghana to explain the origin of a beautiful type of fabric: kente cloth. For a long time, kente cloth was only woven for the kings and queens of the Asante. Today, other people can wear it, but it remains very special.

Kente cloth is woven by hand in long, narrow strips, about 4" wide and 70" long. The narrow strips are sewn together to form a larger piece of fabric. Red, gold, blue, and green are the colors usually used.

Because weaving involves creating a grid of horizontal and vertical threads, the patterns used in kente cloth tend to use geometrical shapes. Many patterns have been given descriptive names and even have some symbolic meaning.

In this activity, you will use a simple loom to weave a narrow strip of fabric. You can work out a design in advance and try to create it on the loom, or you can make the design up as you go along. Stripes of different widths are the easiest patterns to make on this type of loom. Follow these directions to weave your own cloth in the style of kente cloth.

1. Make a simple loom out of heavy card. Take a piece of 5" × 8" cardboard. Mark off a ½" border on all four sides. Place the cardboard so that the long edges are on the sides, with the short edges at the top and bottom. Along the short edges, mark off every ¼" between the borders. Working very carefully, cut ½" slits in the cardboard edge, down as far as the border line. Do the same for both the top and bottom edges.

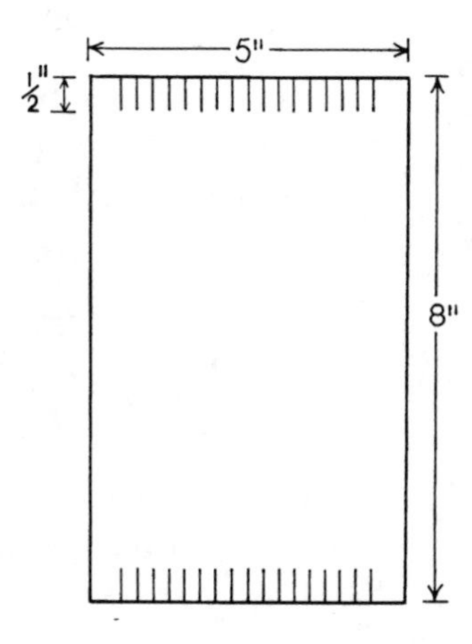

(continued)

Name ____________________ Date ____________________

Ghana: Kente Cloth *(continued)*

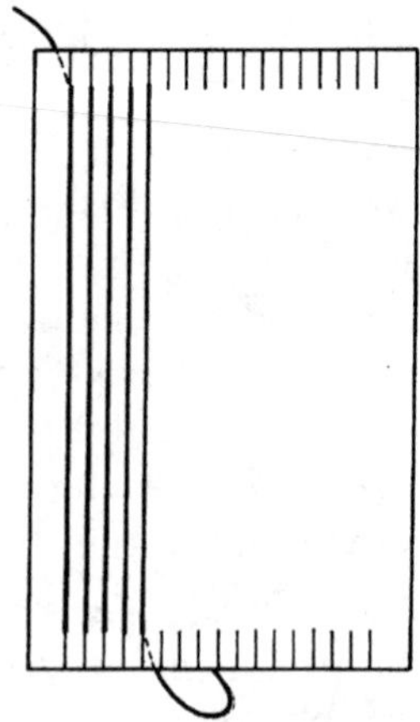

2. The vertical threads in weaving are called the warp threads. To put the warp threads on your loom, start in the upper left corner. Tie a knot near the end of the warp string. Slip the string through the slit nearest the left edge so that the string hangs down the front of the loom and is held in place by the knot at the back. Bring the string down to the lower left slit and pull the string through the slit towards the back of the loom. Run the thread behind the cardboard to the next slit on the bottom edge. Bring the string through to the front and run it up the front of the cardboard to the next slit on the upper edge. Keep running the warp string up and down the cardboard until each slit is threaded. Tie a knot in the end of the string. To keep the warp strings from slipping off, place a strip of masking tape over the top and bottom edges of the loom.

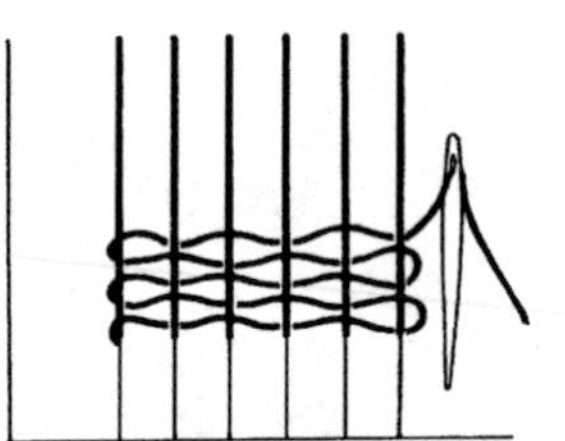

3. To weave the fabric, thread the tapestry needle with a length of embroidery floss. The crossways threads are called the weft threads of the fabric. Starting at one edge of the bottom of the loom, bring the thread over one warp thread, under the next, over the next, and so on until you reach the far edge of the loom.
4. Bring the weft thread around the last warp thread and go back across the loom. This time you will go over the threads you went under on the first row, and under the threads you went over. This is called plain weave, or tabby weave. Be careful not to pull the weft thread too tightly when you wrap it around the outer warp threads, or your fabric will not be a rectangle when it's done; it will be pulled in at the middle.
5. To create a pattern in your fabric, create horizontal stripes by changing the color of the weft thread. Try varying the width of the stripes. You can create a checkerboard effect by going over and under two threads on each row, instead of one. See what other patterns you can create.

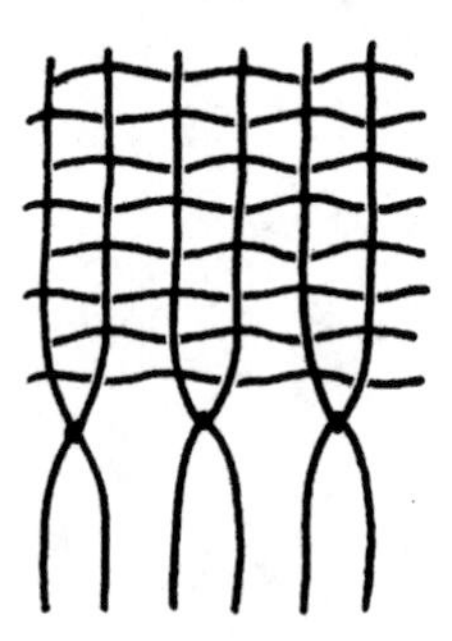

6. When you have completed your weaving, remove it from the loom. The unwoven part of the warp threads will form loops at the ends. You need to bind them off, or your weaving will gradually become loose. You can fold the loops over to the back and sew them down, or you can cut the ends of the loops, then knot pairs of strings together to form a fringe.

Ghana: Akan Coffins

Objectives

Social Studies

- Students will gain an understanding of the different ways different peoples approach the same thing.

Art

- Students will create a functional papier-mâché box in the manner of an Akan coffin.

Materials

Akan Coffins handout
newspapers
colander or sieve
pencils and paper
wallpaper paste
blender or wire whisk
clay
bowl
water
ruler
saucepan
white glue

Background

The history of Ghana goes back for hundreds of years to the great empires of West Africa: Ghana, Mali, and Songhai. In this area, as elsewhere in Africa, rituals and ceremonies are seen as an important way to connect the past and the present.

In most traditional religions a person's ancestors are believed to watch over the family and the community. According to this view of the world, a person's involvement with life does not end with death. It just changes.

Preparation

Prepare the papier-mâché pulp in advance.

1. To make one quart: Tear four large newspaper sheets into small pieces. Place in a container with two quarts of water and let soak overnight.
2. Place the paper and water in a large saucepan. Boil for 20 minutes.
3. Use a whisk to beat the paper until it is soft and pulpy, or process small amounts at a time in a blender.
4. Place the pulp in a strainer. Tap it a few times to shake out the water. Then squeeze it gently until the pulp is a soft moist lump.
5. Put the pulp in a bowl. Stir in two tablespoons of liquid white glue and two tablespoons of wallpaper paste. Stir until the mixture is no longer lumpy.

Procedure

1. Distribute the handout and discuss it with students. Some students may find the project ghoulish and resist working on it. But it is an excellent way of showing students that different cultures have different attitudes, even about death.
2. Working individually, students design their boxes. Check their work at this stage to make sure their designs are appropriate for a modeling medium. The design as a whole should be compact. Fine extensions, like antennae, will be difficult to model and fragile when completed.
3. Students should proceed as directed on the handout.

Variation

Instead of papier-mâché, use self-hardening clay. The finished box will be heavier than papier-mâché, but should otherwise have similar properties.

Do you like chocolate?
Chocolate is made from cacao, and most of the cacao in the world is grown in Ghana and the Côte d'Ivoire.

Name ______________________ Date ______________

Ghana: Akan Coffins

We're all used to ceremonies that celebrate life. When we were children, a ceremony was probably held when we were given a name. As we get older, a ceremony may be held to mark our coming of age in our faith or in our community. Most cultures hold a ceremony when two people decide to marry.

Most cultures also hold some sort of ceremony when people die, but it isn't usually a celebration. In the West, people dress in dark colors. The coffin, a somber wooden box, is draped with a dark cloth. Funerals are generally sad and solemn.

For the Akan people of Ghana, funerals are more than that. A funeral is a family affair. Relatives come from all over the country. Funerals bring cousins together, and allow people to renew and maintain friendships. The whole extended family shares the bills for the funeral. The dead person's relatives use drumming, singing, and dancing to celebrate the beginning of a new life after death. They believe that the spirits of relatives who have died will look after them.

One of the most striking features of an Akan funeral is the coffin. Many people want something more distinctive than a rectangular box. The coffin represents the last glimpse friends will have of the person who has died. Before they die, some people decide they want a coffin that will show something about their personality or their interests. So they choose a design that relates to their lives and hire an artist to create a coffin. For example, cocoa is an important export for Ghana. Wealthy cocoa farmers sometimes choose coffins in the shape of an enormous cocoa pod. The artist carves a coffin in the shape desired, then paints it. The person who has died gets to ride to the funeral in style.

1. In this activity, you are going to make a box inspired by Akan coffins. Choose a three-dimensional object to represent something that interests you. Think about your interests, your studies, and your hobbies. What aspects of your life are important to you? For example, if you love sports, you might choose a football or a basketball shoe. You might choose a book, or a camera, or a fish, depending on your interests. Make a careful drawing of the object. You are going to make it out of papier-mâché, so the basic shape should be fairly simple. You can add details with paint.

2. To make your box hollow, start by forming a 5" × 3" × 1" rectangle of clay. Wrap the clay in plastic wrap. You will form your box around the clay core. Use papier-mâché pulp to build up the sections of the box, shaping it as you go.

3. While the papier-mâché is still wet, cut through it to form a lid. The lid can be just a rectangle cut out of the upper surface of the box, or it could be more structural. Put the lid and the box aside separately to dry.

4. Once your box has dried completely, remove the clay core. Lightly sand the outside of the box if necessary. Then paint it with tempera or acrylic paints.

Ghana: Adinkra Cloth

Objectives

Social Studies

- Students will see how a visual art can be used to transmit culture.

Art

- Students will create printing stamps and print a length of fabric.

Math

- Students will examine print motifs for line and turn symmetry.

Materials

Adinkra Cloth handout
glue
scissors
newspaper
acrylic paint
small wooden blocks or corks
white or light-colored cotton fabric
stamping foam or polystyrene meat trays, cleaned and with the edges cut off

Background

To make adinkra cloth, the Asante carve their designs from pieces of calabash (gourd) shell. Thin pieces of wood, like a tripod, are put into the stamp from behind to form a handle. The ink for printing the cloth is made by boiling tree bark. The fabric is sectioned off in rectangles with a wooden comb dipped in dye. The comb makes a number of parallel lines on the cloth. Once the fabric has been divided up, the adinkra motifs are stamped in the open areas. A single piece of fabric might use just one motif or might combine a number of different symbols.

Procedure

1. Prepare a thick pad of newspaper for each work station. The padding will help the stamp give a stronger impression.
2. Cut the cloth into 12" squares. If you want students to work in groups on larger pieces of fabric, cut it into rectangles 3' x 2'.
3. Distribute the handout and discuss it with students. Point out the symmetry of many adinkra motifs. Discuss the varieties of symmetry—line symmetry and turn symmetry—and see how many of these patterns are symmetrical.
4. Students proceed as directed on the handout.

Name ____ Date ____________________

Ghana: Adinkra Cloth

Adinkra cloth consists of strips of cotton printed with decorative stamps. Although no one really knows the origin of adinkra cloth, the Asante tell a story about how it came to Ghana. The Asante people had a golden stool, which was an important symbol of their leader's power. Adinkera, a neighboring king, admired the stool, and made a copy of it. To the Asante, this was a terrible offense. The golden stool was much more than a beautiful art object. As the symbol of the leader's power, it had a religious significance. Making a copy of the stool was an insult to their leader and to their religion. The Asante went to war with Adinkera. Adinkera was defeated and killed, and the Asante took the printed cloth he was wearing as a trophy of war. This was the first adinkra cloth of the Asante people.

The word *adinkra* means "good-bye" in the language of the Asante. Because of this, adinkra cloth was traditionally used for funeral clothes. Today, it is worn for a variety of occasions.

Like many other aspects of West African decorative arts, the stamps used to make adinkra cloth are more than just attractive to look at. Most of them also have a meaning. They can be used to symbolize something else.

The following are some popular adinkra symbols and their meanings. The first definition is the literal meaning of the words; the second is either the symbolic meaning or shows how the literal meaning can be applied to people's lives.

Gye nyame—symbol of the omnipotence of God.

"Fantum funafu denkyem funafu won afuru bom nso worididi a na wo ko."
"Sharing one stomach, yet they fight over food." Pokes fun at greed.

Nsoroma—a child of the heavens. Symbol of dependence on God.

Nkonsonkonso—a link or chain. Symbol of human relations.

Osram ne nsroumme—the moon and the star. A symbol of loyalty, faithfulness, harmony, and love.

Nyame dua—an altar or place of worship.

Nyeme nwu na mawu—"God does not die, and so I don't die." Symbol of all-knowingness and ever-presence of God.

(continued)

Name ______________________________ Date ____________________

Ghana: Adinkra Cloth *(continued)*

 **Akoma**—the heart. A symbol of love, patience, goodwill, and endurance.

 **Fihankra**—symbol of safety and security at home.

 **Nkyin kyin**—changing oneself, playing many roles.

1. Choose one or two of the adinkra motifs. Draw the design on the stamping foam. Use scissors to cut around the outside lines of the design. If your design includes inner details, use a pen or pencil to compress the foam in those areas.
2. Glue your adinkra designs onto wooden blocks or corks.
3. The typical adinkra cloth is divided off in rectangles, and each area is filled with repeats of one motif. To divide your cloth, dip the edge of a piece of cardboard in ink and press it down on the cloth.
4. Use one motif for each rectangle. Print by dipping your stamp in ink and pressing it on the fabric.

Use a long strip of fabric to make a *gele*, the typical woman's headdress of Ghana.

1. Place the fabric so that it is centered at the back of the head. The two ends should be even when you bring them to the front.
2. Bring the two ends forward and overlap them in front. Bring the ends around to the back and tie a knot at the base of the head.
3. Bring the loose ends back around to the front again, cross them, and tuck the ends into the front or sides of the gele.

Ghana and Côte d'Ivoire: Akan Gold Weights

OBJECTIVES

Social Studies

- Students will understand that trade and economy can affect culture.

Art

- Students will understand the *cire perdue*, or lost wax, method of casting metal.
- Students will make a three-dimensional figure incorporating certain criteria.

Science

- Students will understand a basic method of casting metal.

MATERIALS

Akan Gold Weights handout
modeling wax

BACKGROUND

Peoples of West Africa have been working with metal for over 2000 years. By 300 B.C., people in Nigeria knew how to smelt iron—to get it from rocks and melt away the impurities. Iron was used for practical things, for tools and weapons. But another metal was also important in the history of West Africa: gold. The empires of Ghana and Mali controlled much of the trade in gold with North Africa. When Mansa Musa, who ruled Mali in the 1300's, made a pilgrimage to Mecca, he gave out so much gold in Arabia that gold became plentiful. Because it was suddenly so easy to get, its value went down.

The brass weights of the Akan people were created to measure gold and to show the skills of the artists who created them.

PROCEDURE

1. Distribute the handout and discuss it with students.
2. Distribute the modeling wax. Students proceed as directed on the handout.

VARIATION

Instead of modeling wax, students can use clay or another plastic material to shape their figures.

ASSESSMENT

Did students create a small wax sculpture in the style of an Akan gold weight?

Name ______________________ Date ______________________

Ghana and Côte d'Ivoire: Akan Gold Weights

Akan is the name of a language spoken in Ghana and the Côte d'Ivoire.The area where the Akan people live is rich in gold. Centuries ago, the Akan people learned to dig and pan for gold. Traders came to exchange goods for gold: salt, fabrics, leather, weapons. The gold trade was the basis for several empires in West Africa.

To be able to trade effectively, the Akan needed to be able to measure their gold. They did this by weighing it in a simple balance scale. They placed gold dust in one pan of the scale and a small brass weight in the other.

Because their only purpose was to balance the valuable gold dust, you might think that the brass weights would be very plain. They weren't. Each weight was a sculpture in miniature—a flock of birds on a tree, a porcupine, a fan, a leopard. Most of them were less than two inches long.

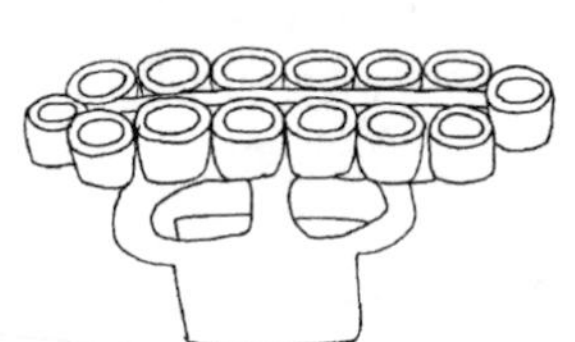

These weights were made using a method called "lost wax." First the sculptor shaped a model for the sculpture out of wax, with all the details wanted in the finished piece.

When the wax model was ready, it was carefully coated in clay. A hollow opening was left in the clay.

Then the whole thing, wax model and clay coating, was placed in a fire. The heat hardened the clay so that it would keep its shape. It also melted the wax, which ran out through the opening in the clay. This left a hollow space inside the clay, exactly the shape of the wax model.

In the next step, the artist poured liquid metal through the opening in the clay so that it filled the hollow space. Once the metal cooled and hardened, the clay covering would be broken away. The metal underneath was an exact duplicate of the wax model.

Although you can't make a metal casting, you can make a wax model like those used by Akan artists.

1. First, decide what you are going to model. Will it be an animal? a geometric shape? a household object? Many Akan gold weights were connected with proverbs or sayings. Perhaps you could illustrate a proverb in your model.

2. Now use the wax to create your model. Remember that the weights used in the gold trade were usually less than 2" long. How much detail can you include in a model that small?

Mali: Griots and the Story of Sundiata

Objectives

English/Language Arts

- Students will understand the importance of oral language as a way of transmitting history.
- Students will create their own oral history.

Social Studies

- Students will understand that history can be transmitted by means other than written history.

Materials

Griots and the Story of Sundiata handout
writing utensils and paper
optional: research materials

Procedure

1. Distribute the handout and discuss with students. Encourage students to think of striking oral presentations they have heard. Point out that a friend describing something that happened at home is just as much an oral presentation as a newscaster reading the news—and may well be a great deal more interesting.

2. If you wish, direct students to do research to find out more details about Sundiata's life.

3. Students work in small groups to develop interesting retellings of Sundiata's story. One student from each group presents to the class.

4. Point out to students that most countries now have written languages, but that storytelling has not disappeared. Why not? What value do oral traditions still have? Can students see any parallels between oral traditions in West Africa and any aspect of culture in this society?

Variation

Assign a different event from the history of a West African nation to each group. The group should research the event, then prepare an interesting narrative to present the information to the class.

Assessment

Did students prepare a vivid oral retelling of an event or story?

Name ______________________ Date ______________

Mali: Griots and the Story of Sundiata

Until Muslim traders brought Arabic writing to the area, West Africa had no written language. But that doesn't mean West Africa had no history. Instead of writing history down, people in West Africa used their memories to keep track of the past. In fact, most communities had a professional oral historian called a *griot*. Part of the griot's job was to memorize history and repeat it so that everyone knew about the past.

This description may make you think of someone standing at the front of a lecture hall, listing names and dates and battles. It shouldn't. That's not the way griots taught history. They recited their stories at the end of the day, when the people of the village gathered to relax. They accompanied themselves on instruments. And they presented history as an exciting narrative.

Have you ever listened to a story being told or read aloud? Some stories don't work very well as listening stories. Sometimes they contain too many big words, or don't really describe things so you can see them clearly. The following is the story of Sundiata, a famous king of Mali, told in a boring way.

> Sundiata was born in the early 1200's in Mali. He was one of twelve brothers who were heirs to the throne of the kingdom of Kangaba. When Sumanguru, ruler of a neighboring state, overran the kingdom, he killed all Sundiata's brothers. Sundiata was spared because he was frail and ill, unable to walk. Sumanguru thought he could not be a threat. However, Sundiata lived to grow strong, and eventually overthrew Sumanguru to become ruler of Mali. He died in 1255.

Here is how one griot, Djeli Mamadou Kouyate, began telling the story of Sundiata.

> Listen then, sons of Mali, children of the black people, listen to my word, for I am going to tell you of Sundiata, the father of the Bright Country, of the savanna land, the ancestor of those who draw the bow, the master of a hundred vanquished kings.

Which version would you rather listen to? Which would be more likely to help you remember the story of Sundiata?

Work with your group to finish the griot's version of the story of Sundiata. Make your retelling lively, so that it would make people want to listen to the whole thing and remember it. Choose a representative to present your version of the story to the class.

Nigeria: Proverbs

OBJECTIVES

Language Arts

- Students will analyze the meaning of unfamiliar phrases to find parallels with English phrases.
- Students will learn that proverbs can carry the wisdom of people from generation to generation.

Social Studies

- Students will understand some of the commonalties between different cultures.
- Students will understand that proverbs and sayings can be used to transmit culture.

MATERIALS

Proverbs handout
paper and pencils

BACKGROUND

Proverbs are part of every spoken language. Comparing proverbs from various parts of the world shows that the same kernel of wisdom can be expressed in different ways. Proverbs often reflect the different cultures that develop them. Many proverbs form part of a code of behavior and are used to transmit rules of conduct within a culture. They also tend to use rhyme, alliteration, and homely imagery—household objects, animals, and the events of everyday life. In North America the best-known use of proverbs is probably *Poor Richard's Almanack,* published annually by Benjamin Franklin from 1732–1757. Many of Franklin's proverbs were reworkings of old European proverbs with a colonial American twist.

Proverbs have been called "the national poetry of the Yoruba." Throughout West Africa they are used to pass on a clear ethical code.

Here are some West African proverbs, with English equivalents.

Some birds avoid the water, ducks seek it.	Different strokes for different folks.
Even the great River Niger must go around an island. (Hausa)	Power has limits.
If the music changes, so does the dance. (Hausa)	One must move with the times.
Each end of the fire has its smoke. (Hausa)	Everything has consequences.

Procedure

1. Distribute the handout and discuss it with students. If you want, you can use some of the proverbs given in the Background section as examples while you model the process. Encourage students to see how the West African proverbs reflect culture.

2. Students then proceed as directed on the handout.

Answers

1. All talk, no action.

2. As the twig is bent, so it grows.

3. Out of the frying pan, into the fire.

4. Birds of a feather flock together.

5. Look before you leap.

6. Money isn't everything; *or,* You can't buy love.

Extension

In West Africa, proverbs are often associated with visual symbols and animal figures. Many of the adinkra symbols in the activity on page 39 are associated with symbols, as are the Akan gold weights in the activity on page 42. Have students design either an adinkra symbol or an Akan gold weight to illustrate one of these proverbs.

Assessment

Were students able to identify similar proverbs in English or at least to rephrase the West African proverbs to sound like English ones?

Name ________________________________ Date ____________________

Nigeria: Proverbs

Proverbs are short, clever sayings. They use picturesque language to express a piece of wisdom. All cultures have developed proverbs. Most proverbs reflect the culture they come from. For example, proverbs from the Sahara area may represent water as valuable, and proverbs from Southeast Asia may talk of crocodiles. Often, the same thought is expressed in proverbs from different cultures. For example, a Nigerian proverb goes, "Some birds avoid the water, ducks seek it." This is similar to the meaning in the English saying "Different strokes for different folks."

The Ibo of Nigeria play a game with proverbs. The first player recites a proverb. The second player must think of a proverb that has a similar meaning and recite that.

Try playing a version of the Ibo proverb game with the following proverbs from Nigeria. See if you can think of an English proverb that means about the same thing as these African ones. If you can't think of an English proverb with a similar meaning, reword the proverbs to sound like English ones.

1. Fine words do not produce food.
2. What the child says, he has heard at home.
3. He fled from the sword and hid in the scabbard.
4. Only birds of the same clan play together on the same tree.
5. Before you tie up a hyena, think how you are going to let it go.
6. He who has people is richer than he who has money.

> What do your parents do if they want you to leave the room, but don't want to say so out loud? Nigerian parents sometimes wink to give kids the message "Off you go."

Nigeria: What's in a Name?

Objectives

English/Language Arts

- Students will see that names can be more than just labels; they can have meaning in and of themselves.

Social Studies

- Students will understand some of the commonalties and differences between naming ceremonies and traditions in different cultures.

Materials

What's in a Name? handout
pencil and paper

Background

The Yoruba people of Western Nigeria tend to use traditional African names for their children. These names have different meanings and purposes depending on events at the time of the child's birth. Many Yoruba names—like Abayomi, "Come to bring joy"—show the importance of children in Yoruba life.

According to tradition, a girl is named on the seventh day after her birth, a boy on the ninth day, and twins on the eighth day. The naming day is a day of celebration, with gifts for the newborn and its parents, and socializing and dancing by all members of the family and community.

During the naming ceremony, the child is made to taste eight things that symbolize the hopes the adults have for the child. Kola nuts stand for good fortune, water means purity, oil stands for power and health, salt means wisdom, honey signifies happiness, and liquor symbolizes wealth and prosperity. The officiating elder whispers the name in the child's ear, then announces the name to the family and friends who have gathered for the ceremony.

Procedure

1. Distribute the handout and discuss it with students.
2. Students proceed as directed on the handout.

EXTENSION

The following list contains some more Nigerian boys' and girls' names and their meanings. If you wish, you can suggest that students choose a Nigerian name to use as they work through the activities in this book.

Girls

Name	Meaning
Abayomi	Come to bring joy
Abimbola	Born to be rich
Adanna	Father's daughter
Adanne	Mother's daughter
Amonke	To know her is to pet her
Ayo	Joy
Baderinwa	Worthy of respect
Ebere	Mercy
Ezigbo	Beloved
Fayola	Good fortune
Famiya	Suffering
Iheoma	A welcome child
Izebe	Long expected child
Kokumuo	This one will not die
Mma	Beauty
Ngozi	Blessing
Nkechinyere	Whichever God gives
Nnennaya	Her father's mother
Nwadiuko	A child is scarce
Obianuju	Born at the time of plenty
Obioma	Kindhearted
Ukanwa	The quest for children

Boys

Name	Meaning
Abayomi	Come to bring joy
Abimola	Born to be rich
Akinlabi	We have a boy
Adisa	One who makes himself clear
Amuza	Can't know everything
Atuegwu	Fearless
Babafumi	Father loves me
Danladi	Born on Sunday
Dibia	Healer
Ehioze	Above people's jealousy
Ekundayo	Sorrow has turned to happiness
Kayode	He brought joy
Modupe	Thank you
Nwamaife	An intelligent child
Obinna	Dear to the father
Ojeumba	Traveler
Okon	Born in the night
Okpara	First born
Ofuome	He does as he boasts
Uba	Wealthy

ASSESSMENT

Were students able to identify classmates who could be accurately given Nigerian names?

Name ______________________________ Date ____________________

Nigeria: What's in a Name?

In most languages, names have meanings. For example, in English the name Margaret means pearl. The name Peter means rock. But we aren't usually given our names because of their meanings. We may be given a certain name because a family member had that name, or because our parents liked the way it sounded.

How much do you know about your name? Who named you? Does your name have a meaning? Were you named after someone? Was there some kind of celebration or ceremony when you were named?

In Nigeria, names are often chosen for their meaning. The naming of a child is an important occasion. Friends and relatives gather to celebrate.

The Yoruba are people who live in Western Nigeria. Here are some Yoruba boys' and girls' names, and their meanings.

________________ **Abiola**—born during the new year

________________ **Ada**—first daughter

________________ **Abegunde**—born during the holidays

________________ **Abidemi**—born during father's absence

________________ **Ajayi**—born facedown

________________ **Alaba**—second child after twins

________________ **Abiodun**—born at the time of war

________________ **Bandele**—born away from home

________________ **Bejide**—born during the rainy season

________________ **Bosede**—born on Sunday

________________ **Dada**—child with curly hair

________________ **Idowu**—first child after twins

________________ **Ige**—born feet first

________________ **Kehinde**—second-born of twins

________________ **Ojo**—a difficult delivery

________________ **Okalawon**—a son born after several daughters

________________ **Taiwo**—first-born of twins

________________ **Yejide**—the image of her mother

(continued)

Name ______________________________ Date ______________

Nigeria: What's in a Name? *(continued)*

Each of these names means something very specific. A Yoruba family would not be likely to name their first child Idowu (first child after twins), as it would not be true.

Go around the room, looking for people who could accurately be given each of these names. See how many Nigerian names would fit your classmates. When you find someone whose birth matches the name, put that person's initials on the line next to the name.

> When you hear the words "oil-exporting countries," do you immediately think of the Middle East? Well, think of Nigeria, too: It is the fourth largest supplier of oil to the United States.

Nigeria: Humor and Politics

Objectives

Art

- Students will design and create masks.

English/Language Arts

- Students will create a play using satire and caricature.

Social Studies

- Students will identify and critique an issue or concern in their environment, either locally or in the world at large.
- Students will understand some of the fundamental commonalties in the ways different cultures address issues.

Music

- Students will use songs and music in a brief play.

Materials

Humor and Politics handout
paper bags
paper and pencils
papier-mâché (see page 35 for recipe)
optional: newspaper or news magazine photographs and caricatures of the same individuals
paints
markers

Background

In most of West Africa, the traditional village structure is rigid. Older men make the rules, younger men and most women follow them. The male elders rule by consensus. The structure is egalitarian for people of the same age and gender and authoritarian for younger and older individuals. Too much personal power among elders is frowned on. But even in an egalitarian setting, some people will be "more equal." One man might be a particularly good speaker or might be wealthier than others. There is always a tendency for some people to try to gain more power. The Okumpa plays act as a sort of authority equalizer.

Given the Afikpo political structure, the young men could not make critical comments in public. The Okumpa play gives them an accepted way of airing their grievances. In many ways, the plays are related to the Western notions of satire, caricature, and political cartoons.

Procedure

1. Distribute the handout and discuss it with students. Brainstorm some of the kinds of things students might object to but feel they cannot affect. The

issues could be global or local, from damage to the ozone layer to a town's refusal to build a bike lane on a scenic road.

2. Explain to students the concepts of satire and caricature. Satire uses devices like irony, sarcasm, and ridicule to expose folly and vice. A caricature is a representation, either in words or images, where the peculiarities of a person or thing are exaggerated, but a general likeness is maintained. Political cartoons often use caricature. If you wish, show students photographs and caricatures of political figures to help them see how artists use exaggeration to make a point.
3. Divide students into groups. Each group is to decide on a topic for a play. Direct students to develop and write their plays. Encourage them to use variety in their handling of the material. Skits can include a narrator, dialogue between characters, and music and songs. Each play should be five or ten minutes long.
4. Distribute mask-making materials. These can be as simple as paper bags and markers or as complex as papier-mâché, depending on time and materials available. Remind students that their masks must include eyeholes and some method of attachment. Students should create masks for all characters in the play.
5. Student groups present their plays to the class.

Extension

Have students present their finished plays to a wider audience. Depending on the individuals involved, you might want to invite some of those criticized to attend. Just remind them that they are supposed to appreciate the performance, not get angry.

Assessment

Did students identify an issue or action and present a short masked play satirizing it?

Bonus Questions Answers

1. Benin — Porto-Novo
2. Burkina Faso — Ouagadougou
3. Côte d'Ivoire — Abidjan
4. Gambia — Banjul
5. Ghana — Accra
6. Guinea — Conakry
7. Guinea-Bissau — Bissau
8. Liberia — Monrovia
9. Mali — Bamako
10. Niger — Niamey
11. Nigeria — Abuja
12. Senegal — Dakar
13. Sierra Leone — Freetown
14. Togo — Lomé

Name ______________________ Date ______________

Nigeria: Humor and Politics

The Afikpo Ibo live in southeastern Nigeria. Traditionally, their villages are ruled by a group of male elders. In theory, all the elders have the same amount of power. All decisions are made by common agreement among them. In practice, of course, one person may get more influence than others—or may want to have more influence. But as a whole, the group agreement system works well. One reason is the Okumpa play.

Okumpa plays are a series of skits and songs. They are put on by the young men of the village. The young men prepare the play in secret, and rehearse at night. When the play is presented, the players all wear masks. The people of the village agree to respect the disguise of the mask. A player wearing a mask is not to be recognized as himself. The mask changes a man from "mortal" to "spirit" as long as the player wears it. As a spirit the player is no longer bound by the ordinary rules of the village. He can say things he wouldn't ordinarily be allowed to say.

The Okumpa players take full advantage of this chance to speak freely. One type of Okumpa play is used to criticize village leaders. The leaders are named in the play and their behavior is held up to ridicule. If a person who is named in an Okumpa play is in the audience, he is not allowed to become angry. In fact, he is expected to give the actors money in appreciation. The Okumpa plays help keep individual elders from trying to become too powerful.

The masks and costumes in the Okumpa play are used to stress that the players are not appearing as themselves. Some of the masks are animals—a goat, a monkey, a bird. Some are stylized human faces. Some are distorted human faces, deliberately made ugly. These ugly masks are often used to represent old men and to symbolize certain virtures.

In Afikpo society young people have no voice in how village affairs are handled. The Okumpa plays give them a way of making their opinions known, and maybe even of changing things. And even if their plays don't have any effect, at least they've let the elders know how they feel.

In our society, young people have very little power. But we have no Okumpa play to let our leaders know what young people think. However, that doesn't mean you can't prepare a play of your own to criticize something.

1. Work in your group to decide on something you think is being handled badly by the people in charge. It could be the quality of the food served in your cafeteria, or poor relations between different countries, or anything in between.

2. Once you have chosen a topic, write a play that says exactly what you think is wrong. Your play should be about five minutes long. Remember that Okumpa plays often use ridicule to make a point. Feel free to exaggerate.

(continued)

Name ______________________________ Date ____________________

Nigeria: Humor and Politics *(continued)*

Think how political cartoonists work. They often pick some part of a person's appearance—say, a big nose, or dark eyebrows—then exaggerate that feature in a drawing. The exaggeration makes it funny, but it can often make the person easier to recognize. So use lots of exaggeration to make your point.

3. Since songs are an important part of the Okumpa plays, you should have some in your play. You can write your own words to a familiar song or create your own music as well as lyrics.
4. Design and make masks for the characters in your play.
5. Present your play to the class.

Bonus Questions

Here are 14 of the countries of West Africa and their capitals. Can you match each country with its capital?

Country		Capital
1. Benin	____	Abuja
2. Burkina Faso	____	Monrovia
3. Côte d'Ivoire	____	Accra
4. Gambia	____	Abidjan
5. Ghana	____	Porto-Novo
6. Guinea	____	Bissau
7. Guinea-Bissau	____	Niamey
8. Liberia	____	Dakar
9. Mali	____	Lomé
10. Niger	____	Conakry
11. Nigeria	____	Freetown
12. Senegal	____	Banjul
13. Sierra Leone	____	Bamako
14. Togo	____	Ouagadougou

Nigeria: Yoruba Numbers

Objectives

Math

- Students will identify number patterns.
- Students will investigate a base 20 system.

Social Studies

- Students will understand that different cultures develop different responses to the same needs.

Materials

Yoruba Numbers handout
Pencils and paper

Background

Like many other number systems, the old Yoruba system is probably based on human digits—fingers and toes, five, tens, and twenties. Each number from one to ten has a name, as do the numbers 20, 30, 200, and 400. The rest are multiples and compounds of these number words. Forty is two twenties, fifty is three twenties less ten, sixty is three twenties, seventy is four twenties less ten, and so on. To count from 20 to 30, you add as far as 24: 20 + 1, 20 + 2, etc. Then the process switches to a subtractive one: 30 – 5, 30 – 4, etc.

In Nigeria today, the complex Yoruba system is no longer used. The decimal system used in most of the world has been adopted.

Procedure

Distribute the handout, and discuss it with students. Then have students proceed as directed on the handout.

Completed Table

1 1	2 2	3 3	4 4	5 5	6 6	7 7	8 8	9 9	10 10
10 + 1 11	10 + 2 12	10 + 3 13	10 +4 14	20 – 5 15	20 – 4 16	20 – 3 17	20 – 2 18	20 – 1 19	20 20
20 + 1 21	20 + 2 22	20 + 3 23	20 + 4 24	30 – 5 25	30 – 4 26	30 – 3 27	30 – 2 28	30 – 1 29	30 30
30 + 1 31	30 + 2 32	30 + 3 33	30 + 4 34	(20 × 2) – 5 35	(20 × 2) – 4 36	(20 × 2) – 3 37	(20 × 2) – 2 38	(20 × 2) – 1 39	20 × 2 40
(20 × 2)+1 41	(20 × 2)+2 42	(20 × 2) + 3 43	(20 × 2) + 4 44	(20 × 3) – 15 45	(20 × 3) – 14 46	(20 × 3) – 13 47	(20 × 3) – 12 48	(20 × 3) – 11 49	(20 × 3) – 10 50

Bonus Question

Roman numerals use both subtraction and addition in number formation.

Assessment

Were students able to successfully identify the pattern of the Yoruba number formation and fill in the blanks on the table?

Name ______________________________ Date ______________

Nigeria: Yoruba Numbers

The number system we use today is a decimal system. It uses ten as a base for forming numbers. We count in multiples of ten—10, 20, 30, 100, 1000. But other cultures have based their number systems on other units besides 10. The ancient Babylonians based their numbers on 60. The Maya of Mexico based their numbers on 20. Many peoples of West Africa also based their number systems on 20.

The Yoruba of Nigeria used a system based on 20, but their system had a twist in the way the number words were formed. We form our number words by a combination of addition and multiplication. When we say "thirteen," we mean "ten plus three." "Forty" could be translated as "ten multiplied by four," or 10×4. "Forty-three" could be "ten multiplied by four, then add three" or $(10 \times 4) + 3$.

The Yoruba number system also uses addition and multiplication, but it uses subtraction, as well. This system has names for the numbers one through ten, and for twenty, thirty, two hundred, and six hundred. The number words are formed using these names. So thirteen is *eeta laa,* "three in addition to ten," or $10 + 3$. But seventeen is *eeta din logun,* "three reduces twenty," or $20 - 3$. Their word for fifty, *aadota,* means "ten reduces twenty in three ways," or $(20 \times 3) - 10$.

This table shows the numbers from 1 to 50. Most of the squares also show how the old Yoruba word for that number was formed, but some have been left blank. Work out the pattern for forming Yoruba number words. Then fill in the blank spaces.

1 1	2 2	3 3	4 4	5 5	6 6	7 7	8 8	9 9	10 10
10 + 1 11	______ 12	10 + 3 13	10 + 4 14	20 – 5 15	20 – 4 16	______ 17	20 – 2 18	20 – 1 19	20 20
20 + 1 21	20 + 2 22	20 + 3 23	20 + 4 24	30 – 5 25	______ 26	30 – 3 27	30 – 2 28	______ 29	30 30
30 + 1 31	30 + 2 32	______ 33	30 + 4 34	(20 × 2) – 5 35	(20 × 2) – 4 36	(20 × 2) – 3 37	(20 × 2) – 2 38	(20 × 2) – 1 39	______ 40
______ 41	(20 × 2) + 2 42	(20 × 2) + 3 43	______ 44	(20 × 3) – 15 45	(20 × 3) – 14 46	(20 × 3) – 13 47	______ 48	(20 × 3) – 11 49	(20 × 3) – 10 50

Bonus Question

Can you think of another well-known number system that uses subtraction to form numbers?

____

Senegal: A Conversation in Wolof

Objectives

Social Studies

- Students will be exposed to simple phrases in another language.

Materials

A Conversation in Wolof handout
paper and pencils
scissors

Procedure

1. Distribute the handout and discuss it with students. Can students identify any patterns in the Wolof words?
2. Students proceed as directed on the handout.
3. When students have had sufficient time to practice, choose one student from each of two different pairs to demonstrate their skills in Wolof for the class. If time allows, have other student pairs recite their greetings in Wolof.

Assessment

Were students able to memorize simple phrases in Wolof and combine them to form a conversation?

Name ______________________________ Date ____________________

Senegal: A Conversation in Wolof

When you think of African people relaxing and talking together, what language do you imagine them using? If you said *African*, think again. Just as there is no one African culture, there is no one "African" language. In fact, almost 1000 different languages are spoken in Africa.

Even within one country, a number of different languages may be spoken. For example, in Senegal the official language is French, but it is spoken by a minority of the population. Most people speak Wolof, the language of the Wolof people. The other leading languages are Malinke, Serer, and Pular. And other languages besides these are also spoken, though often by small numbers of people.

Here are some everyday phrases in Wolof. Working with a partner, prepare flash cards for these phrases. Practice saying them until you can hold a simple conversation in Wolof.

English	Wolof	Pronunciation
Hello	Salaam maaleekuum	[salam-ma-like-um]
Hello (response)	Maaleekuum salaam	[ma-like-um salam]
My name is ________.	Maa ngitud ________ .	[ma-gey-tood]
How are you?	Na nga def?	[na-ga-deaf?]
I am pleased to meet you.	Beg na ci xamelbi	[beg-na-key-cha-mel-bee]
Do you speak Wolof?	Deeg nga Wolof?	[deg na Wolof?]
No, I do not speak Wolof.	Dee ded. Deguma Wolof.	[day-ded. Deg go ma Wolof]
Thank you.	Jéréjëf	[jay-ray jeff]
Good-bye.	Ajé, babenen.	[a-jay, ba-bay-nen]

Guy, *phony*, and many other English words originally came from Wolof.

Sierra Leone: The Game of Haba Gaba

Objectives

Social Studies

- Students will understand some of the common features of games from different cultures.

Math

- Students will apply measuring and quantifying skills to real-life setting.

Materials

ruler
pencil
medium-sized cardboard box
scissors or utility knife
three bean bags (If bean bags are not available, tightly-rolled socks work well.)
optional—to make bean bags: for each bag, two circles of fabric, 3" in diameter; small dried beans or rice; needle; thread

Preparation

If you wish, you can make simple bean bags for this game, or you can show students how to make them. Place two circles of fabric on top of each other, right sides facing out. Sew almost all the way around the edge, leaving a small opening. Slip beans or rice through the opening to fill the bag. Sew opening closed.

Procedure

Distribute the handout and go over it with students. Students brainstorm the different types of games they play or played. Games may include hide-and-seek, giant steps, hacky sack, tic-tac-toe, cat's cradle, and others. Students proceed as directed on the handout.

Name ______________________________ Date ______________

Sierra Leone: The Game of Haba Gaba

In North America, many families have shelves full of games put out by big toy companies, as well as games that are played on computers or on special game machines. Do you ever play games that don't call for a computer or a premade board? What kinds of games are they? What about when you were younger? Did you play simpler games when you were in elementary school? Make a list of all the materials you used for these games. Do they have anything in common?

Usually, the most common feature of these games is that they are easy to play. You don't need any special materials. You can play them with things you have around the house. Games of this kind are played all over the world. All they call for is a few simple materials and the willingness to spend some time playing them.

Young people in West Africa play games like these, too. The following is a simple toss game played in Sierra Leone.

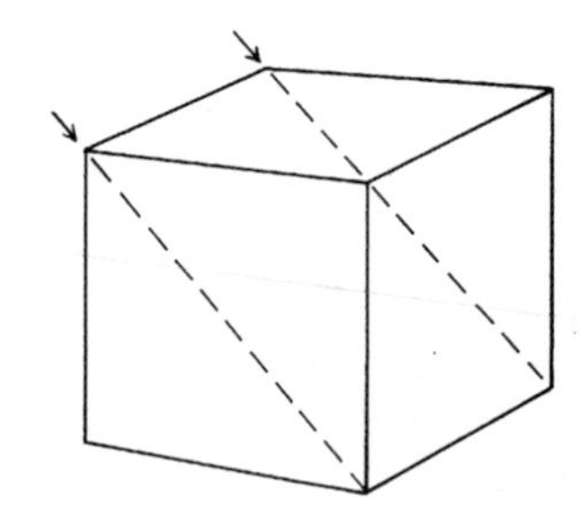

1. Cut the box on the diagonal.
2. Turn the box over so that the cut edge is on the floor.
3. Cut three holes in one slanted side. The top hole should be about 4" across, the second hole about 5" across, and the bottom hole about 6" across. Label the bottom hole 1, the middle hole 2, and the top hole 3.

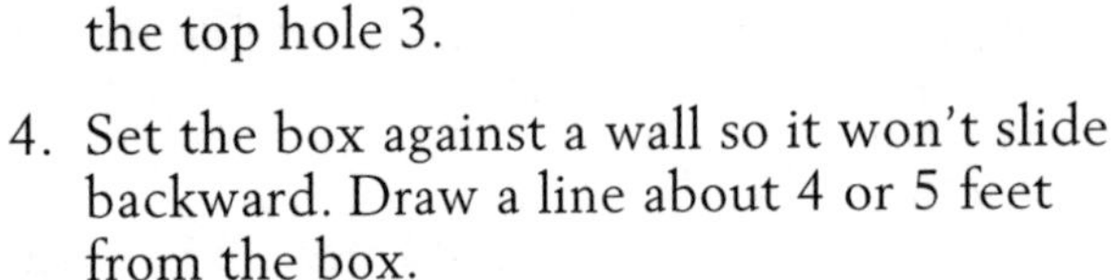

4. Set the box against a wall so it won't slide backward. Draw a line about 4 or 5 feet from the box.
5. To play, players stand behind the line. Each player gets three throws, trying to toss beanbags through the holes in the box. Add up the score. The player with the highest score wins.

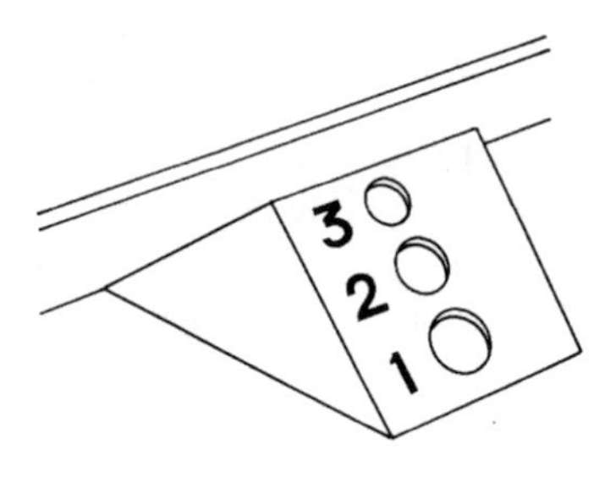

Bonus Question

Does this game remind you of any games you play? Why do you think they are similar?

____

____

Cooking of West Africa: Jollof Rice and Fufu

Objectives

Social Studies

- Students will see how geography can affect different aspects of culture.

Materials

See individual recipes

Background

Cooking styles vary across West Africa as the climate, and thus the crops that can be grown, varies. But some aspects of cooking are the same across much of the region. The staple food is *fufu*, a kind of porridge made of starch, which is rolled into balls and dipped into stews or sauces. The basic starch is made from the root of the cassava melon or the seeds of millet grass, but it can also be rice, or even yams. In poor areas, the roots or seeds are pounded in large wooden mortars; the process can take hours. The sauces used for dipping are usually very spicy, and often contain peanuts and hot peppers. Fish, chicken, and various kinds of meat are often prepared in stews. Okra is a common stew and soup ingredient, as are eggplant and tomatoes. Kabobs, called *kyinkinga*, are made with meat and green peppers, and are flavored with ginger and peanut sauce. All over West Africa, street vendors sell them.

The recipes in this activity give directions for making three typical West African dishes. Plantain chips would usually be eaten as a snack. Fufu can be served with a spicy dipping sauce, or as a bland accompaniment to a main dish. Different versions of Jollof rice are served across West Africa.

Although the main meal is a time to socialize, in some areas the traditional division between men and women is still observed. Men and boys eat together from one dish, and women and girls from another.

Preparation

You may wish to do any slicing and chopping in advance, to save time. For the Jollof rice recipe, you may wish to partially cook the chicken, so that the dish can be prepared within one class period.

Procedure

1. Distribute the handout about West African food and discuss it with the class. Encourage students to consider how West Africa's geography and climate—particularly regarding rainfall—might affect the food people eat.

2. Divide the class into three groups, one for each recipe. Distribute the ingredients and recipe sheets to each group.
3. Students should prepare the recipes as directed.
4. Once all the food is ready, gather around for a West African meal. In traditional West African families, food is eaten from a communal dish. Diners dip into the dish with their hands, a piece of bread, or a ball of fufu for. Fufu, spoons made from gourds are also used. As a concession to Western habits, you may want to allow students to use cutlery and separate dishes. Or if you feel that students would be comfortable eating from a communal dish, you might provide pieces of bread for each student to use in dipping up the rice.

Bonus Question

Because it takes much more land to graze animals for meat than to produce vegetable crops.

Name ______________________________ Date ______________

Cooking of West Africa: Jollof Rice and Fufu

In most parts of North America, there are four distinct seasons in the year: spring, summer, autumn, and winter. In most of West Africa there are two: the rainy season and the dry season.

During the six or seven months of the dry season, no rain falls at all. In the areas near rivers, crops can be grown during the dry season. Farmers take water from the rivers to irrigate their fields. But in the rest of West Africa, crops cannot be grown when it does not rain.

At the end of the dry season, the winds change. Instead of blowing from the northeast, across the Sahara Desert, the winds start to blow from the south, across the Atlantic Ocean. The wet air from the ocean causes huge rainstorms. The land below is drenched.

Farmers take advantage of the water to grow crops: millet, yams, corn, cassava, and peanuts. They need to grow and store enough food in the rainy season to feed people year-round.

Like cooking in other areas, West African cooking is based on the crops grown there. It relies heavily on vegetables and grains. Peanuts and hot red peppers are used as seasonings, and the food is often very spicy. The traditional custom is to have one large meal a day, with light snacks during the rest of the day. The main meal is a time to socialize with family and neighbors.

Meals aren't usually served on a separate dish for each person, as they are in the West. Instead, the main dish is put in a large bowl in the middle. To eat, people dip their hands or a piece of bread or a ball of *fufu* (a kind of dumpling) into the dish, scoop up some food, and eat.

West Africa isn't easy for left-handers. It's considered very rude to eat with your left hand, especially from the common pot. It's an insult to shake hands with the left hand. And accepting a gift with the left hand is unforgivable.

Bonus Question

Why do you think much of West African cooking uses vegetables and grains, and not much meat?

____

____

Name ______________________________ Date ______________

Cooking of West Africa: Jollof Rice and Fufu *(continued)*

Hot Plantain Chips

Plantains are a kind of banana. Unlike most bananas, they are not good to eat raw. In this dish, plantains are fried in thin rounds, to be eaten as a snack.

Ingredients

4 firm plantains
4 tsp. lemon juice
oil for frying
4 tsp. ground ginger
4 tsp. cayenne pepper

Implements

sharp knife
cutting board
2 bowls
heavy frying pan
slotted spoon
stove
paper towels

1. Slice the plantains into 1/2" thick rounds. Place them in a bowl. Sprinkle lemon juice over the pieces, stirring to moisten them.
2. In another bowl, combine the ginger and cayenne pepper. Roll the pieces of plantain in the mixture, a few pieces at a time. They should be thinly coated in the spice mixture.
3. Pour 1/4" oil into the frying pan. Place the pan over medium heat. Heat until a drop of water sprinkled in the pan sputters in the oil.
4. Place the plantain pieces in the skillet. Fry until they are crisp and golden.
5. Remove the plantain from the frying pan with a slotted spoon. Place them on paper towels to cool slightly. Serve hot.

Name ______________________________ Date ______________

Cooking of West Africa: Jollof Rice and Fufu *(continued)*

Yam Fufu

Fufu is a basic food in most of West Africa. It is usually made from cassava or millet, but it can also be made from other starchy foods. First the food is boiled. Then it is pounded in a wooden mortar until it is smooth and sticky. To eat, diners dip their hands into the bowl of fufu and grab a handful. Then they roll it into a ball between their hands. Fufu is often served with a spicy dipping sauce.

This recipe is for a version of fufu made with yams. Instead of a wooden mortar and pestle, you will use a food processor to break up the starch.

Ingredients

2 lbs. yams
1/4 tsp black pepper
1/4 tsp salt
1 tsp. butter

Implements

large saucepan
food processor
large bowl
stove

1. Half fill the saucepan with cold water. Put the yams in the water, and put the pan over high heat on the stove. Bring to a boil. Cook for 25 minutes or until the yams are soft.
2. Remove the yams and let them cool slightly. Peel the yams, then mash them together with the other ingredients.
3. Place the mixture in the food processor. Run the processor briefly to remove any lumps. Do not puree.
4. Place the fufu in a bowl. Beat with a wooden spoon until it is smooth. The mixture should be sticky and slightly resilient.
5. Shape the fufu into balls with your hands. Serve warm.

Name ______________________ Date ______________________

Cooking of West Africa: Jollof Rice and Fufu *(continued)*

Jollof Rice

Although this dish probably takes its name from a region of Senegal, it is found all over West Africa. The word *Jollof* in a recipe always means that the rice is cooked with the rest of the ingredients, not separately. Different areas make different versions of Jollof rice.

Ingredients

1 chicken, cut up
2 cups water
2 small cans tomatoes, with liquid
1/8 tsp. salt
1/8 tsp. pepper
1 cup sliced green beans
1 cup uncooked rice
1/4 tsp. cinnamon
1/4 tsp. ground red pepper
3 cups coarsely shredded cabbage
2 sliced onions

Implements

measuring cups
measuring spoons
large saucepan
stove
knife

1. Place chicken, tomatoes, water, salt, and pepper in a large pan over high heat. Bring to a boil. Reduce heat, cover, and simmer for 30 minutes.
2. Remove the chicken from the pan. Stir in the rice, cinnamon, and red pepper. Add the remaining ingredients, and return the chicken to the pan. Return to a boil.
3. Reduce heat and cover. Simmer until the chicken is thoroughly cooked, 20–30 minutes.

Resources

General Resources

Bascomb, William. *African Art in Culture Perspective.* New York: W.W. Norton, 1973.

Blauer, E. Hagale. *Children of the World: Nigeria.* Milwaukee: Gareth Stevens Publishing, 1992. Day-to-day life in Nigeria from the viewpoint of a 10-year-old.

Caraway, Caren. *African Designs of the Congo, Nigeria, the Cameroons, and the Guinea Coast.* Owings Mills, MD: Stemmer House, 1986.

Catchpole, Brian. *History of West Africa in Maps and Diagrams.* Collins Educational, 1983.

Drewal, Henry. *Yoruba: Nine Centuries of African Art and Thought.* New York: The Center for African Art, 1989.

Haskins, Jim, and Joann Biondi. *From Afar to Zulu: A Dictionary of African Cultures.* New York: Walker and Company, 1995.

Hintz, Martin. *Enchantment of the World: Ghana.* Chicago: Children's Press, 1987.

Horizon History of Africa, The. New York: American Heritage Publishing Co., Inc. 1971. Illustrated history includes examples of African literature, both oral and written.

http://www.africaonline.com/AfricaOnLine/kidsonly/quiz.html
Quiz to show students how much they know about Africa.

Levy, Patricia. *Cultures of the World: Nigeria.* New York: Marshall Cavendish, 1993.

Lumpkin, Beatrice, and Dorothy Strong. *Multicultural Science and Math Connections: Middle School Projects and Activities.* Portland, ME: J. Weston Walch, Publisher, 1995.

McKissack, Patricia, and Fredrick McKissack. *The Royal Kingdoms of Ghana, Mali, and Songhay: Life in Medieval Africa.* New York: Henry Holt & Company, 1994.

Price, Christine. *Made in West Africa.* New York: E.P. Dutton & Co., Inc., 1975. Illustrated with photographs and drawings, this book gives an overview of West African art, with chapters on textile arts, pottery, clay sculpture, metal sculpture, and more.

Senegal in Pictures. Minneapolis: Lerner Publications Company, 1988.

Sutherland, Dorothy B. *Enchantment of the World: Nigeria.* Chicago: Children's Press, 1995.

Zaslavsky, Claudia. *Multicultural Mathematics.* Portland, ME: J. Weston Walch, Publisher, 1993.

Zimmerman, Robert. *Enchantment of the World: The Gambia.* Chicago: Children's Press, 1994.

West African Folktales

Anderson, David. *The Origin of Life on Earth: An African Creation Myth.* Mount Airy, MD: Sights Productions, 1991. Lyrical retelling of a Yoruba creation myth.

Fairman, Tony. *Bury My Bones but Keep My Words: African Tales for Retelling.* New York: Henry Holt, 1992.

Music of West Africa

Adzinyah, Abraham, Dumisani Maraire, and Judith Tucker. *Let Your Voice Be Heard: Songs from Ghana and Zimbabwe.* (book and audiocassette) Danbury CT: World Music Press, 1986.

Bebey, Francis. *African Music: A People's Art.* Josephine Bennett, trans. New York: Lawrence Hill & Company, 1975.

Berliner, Paul. *Soul of Mbira,* Chicago: The University of Chicago Press, 1981.

Dietz, Betty W. *Musical Instruments of Africa.* New York: The John Day Company, 1965.

Wilson, Greg Gule. *The Drummer's Path.* (book and audiocassette) Rochester, VT: Destiny Books, 1992.

Appliqué Art of Dahomey

Adler, Peter, and Nicholas Barnard. *Asafot: African Flags of the Fante.* New York: Thames and Hudson, 1992.

Dendel, Esther Warner. *African Fabric Crafts: Sources of African Design and Technique.* New York: Taplinger, 1974.

Price, Christine. *Made in West Africa.* New York: E.P. Dutton & Co., Inc., 1975.

Building a House

Courtney-Clarke, Margaret. *African Canvas.* New York: Rizzoli, 1990. Photographs of vernacular African architecture.

Denyer, Susan. *African Traditional Architecture.* New York: Holmes & Meier, 1978.

Kente Cloth

Hintz, Martin. *Enchantment of the World: Ghana.* Chicago: Children's Press, 1987.

http://www.erols.com/kemet/kente.htm Describes cloth and gives full-color samples of patterns, explaining pattern names and meanings.

Price, Christine. *Made in West Africa.* New York: E.P. Dutton & Co., Inc., 1975.

Adinkra Cloth

Price, Christine. *Made in West Africa.* New York: E.P. Dutton & Co., Inc., 1975.

Griots

Bertol, R. *Sundiata: The Epic of King Lion*. New York: Crowell, 1970.

Chinweizu. *Voices from 20th Century Africa: Griots and Towncriers.* London: Faber and Faber, 1988.

Proverbs

Knappert, Jan. *The A–Z of African Proverbs.* Karnak House, 1989.

Leslau, Charlotte. *African Proverbs.* White Plains, NY: Peter Pauper, 1985.

What's in a Name?

Baird, K.E. (ed.). *Names from Africa: Their Origin, Meaning, and Pronunciation*. Chicago: Johnson Publishing, 1972.

Damali, Nia. *Golden Names for an African People.* Atlanta, GA: Blackwood Press, 1986.

Madubuike, Ihechukwu. *A Handbook of African Names.* Colorado Springs, CO: Three Continents Press, 1994.

Stewart, J. *African Names: Names from the African Continent for Children and Adults.* New York: Carol Publishing Group, 1993.

Humor and Politics

Ottenberg, Simon. "Humorous Masks and Serious Politics Among Afikpo Ibo," *African Art and Leadership*, Douglas Fraser and Herbert M. Cole, eds. Madison, Milwaukee, and London: The University of Wisconsin Press, 1972.

Yoruba Numbers

Zaslavsky, Claudia. *Africa Counts: Number and Pattern in African Culture.* Boston: New York: Prindle, Weber & Schmidt, Inc., 1973.

Cooking in West Africa

Hultman, Tami, ed. *Africa News Cookbook: African Cooking for Western Kitchens.* Penguin, 1985.

Nabwire, Constance and Bertha Montgomery. *Cooking the African Way.* Minneapolis: Lerner, 1989.

Glossary

adinkra cloth	cotton cloth printed with decorative stamps
aerophone	wind instrumentgm
Anansi stories	folktales told in West Africa which often feature Anansi the spider, a trickster character
appliqué	fabric decoration technique in which small pieces of cloth are stitched—applied—to a larger piece of cloth
Asantehene	king of the Asante people
chordophone	instrument that uses a vibrating string to create sound
cire perdue	metal-casting technique in which a model is made of wax, then surrounded in clay and subjected to heat. The melted wax runs out of the clay surround, creating a detailed mold. Molten metal is poured into the mold, then the clay is broken off the outside, leaving a metal replica of the original wax model.
fufu	starchy food staple throughout West Africa
gele	woman's headdress
griot	professional singer and storyteller
haba gaba	child's game played in Sierra Leone
idiophone	instrument that does not need a membrane, reed, or string to produce sound
ishaka	musical instrument, rattle
kente cloth	cloth made in Ghana in which long, narrow strips of patterned cloth are woven and sewn together to make larger pieces of fabric
kora	musical instrument, a kind of harp
lost wax	see cire perdue
Mansa Musa	fourteenth-century ruler who made Mali known in Europe and the Middle East
mbira	musical instrument, sometimes described in the West as a thumb piano
membranophone	musical instrument that uses a stretched membrane to produce sound
Okumpa play	satirical play performed in parts of Nigeria as political commentary
Sundiata	leader who established the kingdom of Mali in the early 1200's
warp	vertical threads in weaving, strung on the loom before weaving starts
weft	horizontal threads in weaving, added onto the warp threads as the weaving progresses

Who's Who in West Africa

Some culture groups of West Africa, listed by their primary areas of residence.

Benin	Adja, Aizo, Ewe, Fon, Somba
Burkina Faso	Bobo, Dogon, Gurunsi, Lobi, Mossi, Nankani
Gambia	Fula, Jola, Serahuli, Wolof
Ghana	Ahanta, Akan, Asante (Ashanti), Dagomba, Envalue, Ewe, Fanti, Ga, Gonja, Moshi, Nzima, Twi
Guinea	Dialonke, Kpele, Koranki, Malinke, Susu, Toma
Guinea-Bissau	Balante, Mandyako, Parpels
Côte d'Ivoire	Agni, Akan, Asante (Ashanti), Baule, Dan, Guro, Kru, Kwakwa, Senuto
Liberia	Golla, Kpele, Kru, Vai
Mali	Bambara, Dogon, Malinke, Marka, Minianka, Peul, Senuto
Niger	Beriberi-Manga, Djerma, Hausa, Kanuari, Marka, Minianka, Senuto, Tubu
Nigeria	Edo, Hausa, Ibibio, Ibo, Igala, Igbo, Ijan, Kunari, Nupe, Tiv, Yoruba
Senegal	Diola, Lebu, Malinke, Serer, Tukulor, Wolof
Sierra Leone	Mende, Teme, Vai
Togo	Akposo, Ewe, Gurma, Kabrai, Kotokoli, Lamba, Loso, Mina, Moba, Wati, Yoruba